OUT OF
THE TEST TUBE

The alchemist laid the foundations of chemistry.

OUT OF
THE TEST TUBE

THE STORY OF CHEMISTRY

BY HARRY N. HOLMES, PH.D., LL.D.

Oberlin College

Author of: Have You Had Your Vitamins? General
Chemistry; Laboratory Manual of General Chemistry;
Introductory College Chemistry; Outline of Qualitative
Analysis; Introductory Colloid Chemistry; Laboratory
Manual of Colloid Chemistry; Strategic Materials and
National Defense; *co-author of:* Elements of Chemistry.

FIFTH EDITION, REVISED AND EXPANDED

103 Illustrations

EMERSON BOOKS, INC., NEW YORK
1962

Fifth Edition, Revised and Expanded

Second Printing, 1959
Third Printing, 1962

LIBRARY OF CONGRESS CATALOG CARD NUMBER: 57-5762

Manufactured in the United States of America

DEDICATED TO

MARY S. HOLMES

CONTENTS

PREFACE

WHILE YOU yawn comfortably in your easy chair, chemistry wages desperate battles on many fronts—against man's insect enemies, yet dominant on earth; against disease bacteria that have from time to time threatened to exterminate the race of men; against the frowns and mysteries of Nature.

The weapons are drawn, not from scabbard, quiver or cartridge belt, but from the test tube. Some are used quietly by physician and surgeon in the fight with Death, others are violent in the hands of engineers.

There have been impressive victories in some salients like the glorious chemical conquest of the air by which limitless atmospheric nitrogen can be converted into fertilizers and explosives.

The struggle against rocks, reefs, and mountains is being won with chemical forces released from high explosives to make mining, road-building, tunneling, navigation cheaper and safer. But red rust is only half conquered and the chemist has failed miserably to duplicate the skill of the green leaf in converting sunbeams into food and fuel.

For a time it seemed that the motor age would pass with the exhaustion of oil supplies, but that particular spectre has been driven, by the research chemist, into the shadows of a far distant future. In the meantime nations manœuver to gain control of oil fields and of those mineral deposits that mean world power. Each country strives to become self-sufficient. Germany broke the camphor monopoly of Japan by synthesis, from turpentine, of this essential ingredient of picture films, and our own people have now learned how to make synthetic rubber of good quality.

*   *   *   *

If you are one of those intelligent, yet non-technical people who have some interest in chemistry, who would like

ix

to penetrate beyond its "wonders" to an appreciation of its methods:

If you want to understand our research, our reasoning, in order that you may relate chemistry to daily life, to economics, to social relations, to the arts, to national defense, and to world affairs:

Then to you, in your easy chair, this book is dedicated.

I

THE UPWARD SWEEP

A CÆSAR enjoyed breakfast in your house this morning. Born to the purple, accustomed to levy upon remote regions of an empire for luxuries to gratify his fancies, wont to think of his royal presence as the center of a wide world, he started the day right with a liberal use of soap in the bath. No thought did he give to the chemical origin of soap or the involved chemistry of its cleansing function, yet when an alloy steel razor blade drew blood he was quick to seek antiseptic safety in the well-stocked medicine cabinet.

For the imperial breakfast, agricultural and horticultural minions a thousand miles distant had labored and a vast network of transportation lines converged. His morning paper collected in his hand the world news that raced along a thousand wires and his telephone waited for royal speech with any one of millions. After breakfast Cæsar stepped into a luxurious, rubber-tired chariot, cracked the master's whip over a hundred chemical horses, and was drawn swiftly to scenes of work or play.

At every step in this well-begun, modern day he utilized chemical materials, chemically improved, and chemical processes as simple as the explosion of gasoline or as complex as the digestion of the royal breakfast.

You are that Cæsar and this chemical world is still yours to command.

Man has climbed a long way up from savagery, up from superstitious fears of natural forces, up from the delusion of coincidence, since he quit swinging from tree to tree by prehensile tail. Our primitive ancestors were slow to observe closely, slow to classify and compare observations, and slower still to base sound predictions of future behavior of creatures or materials upon such observations.

In short, the scientific method of thinking did not dawn upon the race at a very early date. The earliest known document in the history of science is a treatise on surgery written in Egypt nearly 5000 years ago.

The Mines Magazine

FIG. 1. Man has climbed a long way since those days.

Through earlier ages countless thousands of hunters must have roasted their kill by fires accidentally built on earth rich in iron ore, before one, thinner-skulled than the others, returning to dig a final morsel of roasted bear from the glowing charcoal, observed a soft heavy lump that could be hot-hammered into shapes. The Age of Iron dawned.

FIG. 2. Egyptian artisans.

Ancient Egypt was probably first to develop arts and industries based upon some sort of crude chemistry. At any rate we are certain that 5000 years ago the Egyptians worked with gold, copper, lead, silver, tin, mercury, brass, and bronze. "The coppersmith had become so expert in 2750 B.C., during the Fifth Dynasty, that it was not too great a task to hammer out and form pipes of copper for the rain-water drains of the temple of King Sa-hu-Re at Abusir. . . . When Borchard uncovered the ruins in 1907, one length of the copper pipe was discovered and removed. It is now in the Museum at Berlin."

Egyptian ladies blackened eyebrows and eyelashes with the natural sulfides of lead and antimony and used ground malachite in cosmetics. Dwellers along the Nile four or five thousand years ago were skilled in tanning leather, making glass and enamels, and in preparing a few natural dyes. Mummy cloths of that period give tests for indigo. Nor were these people without some medical art. Our own children may be interested in the fact that the compulsory taking of castor

FIG. 3. The glass blowers of Thebes.

oil by the younger generation was quite the thing in the best Egyptian families of 2000 B.C. Nor is there any question of the antiquity of the art of fermentation.

But, as Alexander Findlay observes, the ancient Egyptians were intensely practical and felt no urge to pursue truth for truth's sake; rather were they eager to increase the comfort and improve the amenities of everyday life.

In contrast to the Egyptians the ancient Greek philosophers from the sixth century B.C. attempted to solve all problems by abstract reasoning, but they had neither the patience nor temperament necessary for the slow accumulation of facts nor the means requisite for accurate experimental investigation. As Francis Bacon put it, "Aristotle had made up his mind beforehand. He did not consult experience in order to make right propositions and axioms, but when he had settled his system to his will, he twisted experience round and made her bend to his system."

At Alexandria, which had become the cultural center of the world, there was fused the abstract learning of the Greeks with the practicalism of the Egyptians and the mysticism of Persians and Chaldeans. After the stupid destruction of the magnificent libraries of this great city in 415 A.D. by the Roman emperors, scholars fled to the four quarters of the globe. The Arabs later protected them and developed their crude "chemia" into "alchemy" which they preserved while Western Europe was ravaged by Goths, Vandals, and Huns. El Geber, master alchemist at the court of Harun al-Rashid, in the eighth century wrote many books in which he taught that the various metals differed only in their proportions of mercury and sulfur. Aristotle, on the other hand, had accounted for all forms of matter as due to varying proportions of the properties of Fire, Earth, Air, and Water, with perhaps a fifth or "Quintessence."

This Arab learning was carried into Spain by the conquering Moors in the eighth century, fortunately for a Europe doomed to centuries of the Dark Ages. The blind acceptance of the doctrines of Aristotle as all-sufficient, the frown of the Church upon scientific investigation, and a revival of belief in magic and occult forces almost stopped the wheels of world progress.

Although alchemy degenerated into the pretended art of transmuting lead and other cheap metals into gold by the aid of the Philosopher's Stone and, "in the hands of the unscrupulous, become an agency for preying upon the credulity and avarice of kings and commons alike" it did discover and hand down through the centuries many valuable properties, reactions, and chemical methods.

There had always been a search for the youth-restoring Elixir of Life so the turbulent Paracelsus was able, in the sixteenth century, to direct alchemy into the field of medical chemistry. About the same time Sir Francis Bacon emphasized the newer scientific method of thinking. In the next century Robert Boyle of Ireland definitely broke with alchemy and prepared the way for analysis of substances.

Chemistry finally came into bud, if not quite into bloom, as an exact science when Joseph Black of England in 1755 actually weighed materials at various stages of chemical

A—Large vat.   B—Plug.   C—Small tub.   D—Deep ladle.
E—Small vat.   F—Caldron.

FIG. 4. The old way of making soda ash. From Agricola's Re Metallica, translated by Herbert and Lou Henry Hoover.

change. Then, shortly afterwards, Lomonossov in Russia and Lavoisier in France were able, by exact weighing of all the materials consumed and all the products, to explain the mystery of burning, of combustion. More of that in another chapter.

One is tempted to write the "ways of the Chemist" as "weighs of the Chemist." Certain it is that without exactness in measurement chemistry would be a sorry science. How shallow was van Helmont's reasoning when he declared that the new growth, some 164 pounds, in a willow planted in a box of weighed earth was due entirely to the water added during five years of growth. The earth lost only two ounces. Clever logic, until a century later Priestley in England proved that the carbon dioxide of the air is an important part of plant food.

Lavoisier in France well deserved the title "Father of Modern Chemistry" for he interpreted the cruder chemistry of the past and made it a science. It is easy to remember that this flowering of a science appeared with the American and the French Revolutions. Priestley, the argumentative clergyman in England, Cavendish, the London millionaire, Scheele, the Swedish drug clerk, and Lavoisier, the martyr, were leading pioneers in the movement. Martyr is the right word for the brilliant Frenchman for he was guillotined on trumped-up charges, his real faults in the eyes of the revolutionaries being his wealth and aristocratic birth.

A. D. Little, with good reason, insists that modern chemical industry began with the invention of the Le Blanc soda process. To be sure soda lakes in Egypt and elsewhere were known from the earliest times but the chief source in Europe prior to 1791 was the barilla or ash of sea plants from Spain. Those were troublesome days in France, so to secure a more certain supply of this soda, or sodium carbonate, so important in the manufacture of glass, soap, and other essentials, the French Academy offered a great prize to the man who could devise a new and suitable method of manufacture. Le Blanc won but, like Lavoisier, came to a tragic end. Revolutionaries seized his factory and drove the heart-broken inventor to suicide in the poorhouse.

The real winner of the prize was England and, ultimately, chemical industry in general. And so civilization moved on at an accelerated rate, with clearer vision from cheaper glass and, if not a cleaner conscience concerning poor Le Blanc, at least a cleaner skin from cheaper soap.

England had the foresight to adopt this process, using such raw materials as salt, sulfuric acid, coal and limestone,

Mathieson Alkali Co.

FIG. 5. In 1791 Nicholas LeBlanc won the prize of 2400 livres offered by l'Academie des Sciences de Paris for his process of making soda ash from salt. He never received his prize money, however. During the French Revolution LeBlanc's patents were voided and his plant wrecked by a mob. In dire poverty, in 1806, he ended his life by suicide.

and at once stimulated the very anemic sulfuric acid industry. As it happened, the British cotton textile industry, which had grown like a mushroom with the advent of new textile machinery and Watt's steam engine, was loudly demanding cheaper alkali and acid and better bleaching agents. To make it a duet, if not a chorus, the paper industry, leaping to life after Fourdrinier's invention of a continuous web paper machine about 1800, shouted for more acid and alkali in the bleaching of paper pulp. Fortunately the mere mixing of soda and lime in water yields sodium hydroxide, caustic soda, as the public calls it.

Now observe how events in pure and applied chemistry were working together at the turn of the century. The Dutch, in harmony with their religion of cleanliness, had dominated European bleaching with a tedious process of treating the cloth with sour milk and alkali, of washing and sunning while pocket book and patience were kept under strain for eight months. But with the rebirth of chemistry sulfuric acid was substituted for sour milk, and cheaper alkali used. Then in rapid succession came Scheele's discovery of chlorine in 1774 and Berthollet's application of this poisonous gas to cloth bleaching the next year, and in 1799 Tennant's treatment of lime with chlorine to make the safer and more convenient "bleaching powder." If all the cotton cloth in Britain today had to be spread out on the grass for bleaching by sun a passing aviator might mistake the island for a huge circus tent.

Up to 1828 it was considered hopeless, if not sacrilegious, for man to attempt to synthesize the thousands of compounds built up by plants and animals by the aid of "vital force." Then came the epoch-making Wöhler in Germany who prepared ammonium cyanate from dead or inorganic materials and transformed it in a test tube into urea, identical with that secreted by the living human body. It was a dramatic discovery, discredited for years by great scientists but finally recognized as a rolling back of horizons to disclose a new and limitless world. Organic chemistry or, as we often call it, carbon chemistry, has now prepared for us more than 500,000 different substances, all with carbon as their center and all previously supposed to be associated with the life process. Probably all other inorganic or "dead substances" could be numbered well under 50,000.

Yes, out of the test tube has come a wealth of beautiful,

useful, merciful products that would have dazzled Aladdin. Chemical synthesis rises to a magnificent creation of things that never were before on land or sea. God is not through with His great task—He has, within a century or two, taken the chemist into partnership—and the chemist carries on.

We chemists are radicals, always voting for change— always against any *status quo* of Nature. To us a static world is uninteresting—and dead as a granite boulder. Living creatures return to dust and death and out of the soil rise flowers with enchanting color and fragrance, all a beautiful series of chemical changes or transformations. The modern chemist emulates Nature and likewise converts waste into the useful, dirt into beauty. If you doubt this compare coal dust, or its tar, with the thousands of coal tar dyes so distracting to the rainbow.

Slosson urged us "not to imitate Nature but to watch her as a treacherous and unsleeping foe, for at any moment and in spite of all our vigilance she may wipe out the human race by famine, pestilence or earthquake and within a few centuries obliterate every trace of its achievement." Consequently the chemist improves upon Nature.

Never forget that Pasteur was a chemist. Implored by France to explain and cure a costly disease of silkworms and to prevent certain undesirable fermentations in French wines, he accomplished his tasks and in so doing founded the science of modern medicine as well as the modern industry of food preservation, the canning industry, the pasteurization of milk and, in part, the purification of public water supplies.

And now, after science has striven mightily and achieved greatly, the Machine is blamed for all the ills and faults of civilization. Why the Age of the Machine any more than the Age of Chemistry is not clear. The machine could not exist but for the art of chemistry in constructing its rods and levers, its wheels and cylinders and wires.

Keyserling, Spengler, Canby and other pessimists see life brought by the machine to a monotonous level, individualism crushed, freedom gone. Others long for the "good old days" and the "simple life." It is to be feared that the traditions of life in the glorious Greece of the Golden Age and even in the England of a century ago have mellowed with time. Though the Greek freeman may have enjoyed a rich life, his five slaves were not so privileged. In 1825 the workmen of London were envied by all the laborers of Europe, yet the English working day numbered fifteen hours of toil. Add to this a few hours for sleep and for eating and discover how much time was left for culture, contemplation, recreation, or things of the spirit.

The experience of the United States in the past eighty-five years, insists Dr. Karl Compton, proves that scientific research and engineering development created more jobs than it destroyed. Directly or indirectly an army gains its subsistence from the following very modern industries:

Automobiles	Rayon
Electricity	Petroleum refining
Telephones	Coal tar
Atomic energy	Aluminum
Airplanes	Magnesium
Synthetic rubber	Plastics

What would those who indict the Machine have advised when England's forests disappeared in the reign of Queen Elizabeth and the coal mines became flooded with water beyond the power of horse-pumps to remove? How fortunate for non-scientific critics of today that this crisis, so acute in the early eighteenth century, was not theirs to meet. Two engineers, Newcomen and Savery, solved England's problem with the invention of a steam-pump, which was later improved greatly by James Watt. This same steam engine was needed to force into the iron furnace enormous quantities of air beyond the resources of the crude bellows operated by animal power. And there are those who call this invention a calamity, for with it began the Age of Power.

"A tool is but the extension of a man's hand; a machine is a complicated tool and he that invents a machine augments the power of a man and the well-being of mankind." So said Henry Ward Beecher.

W. R. Whitney, great research director, asks us to "look at the Nile laborer, pumping water by his own muscle power. It takes all his time to earn the food he eats—we can't expect much from his brain. An electric pump will set that man free.

FIG. 6. A drive on the Appian Way in 200 B.C. was excellent for a torpid liver.

Perhaps, you say, he isn't ready for freedom. Then that is a problem not for industry but for education."

This from the man who doesn't want to go to Heaven if there are no problems there.

Scientific research, much of it chemical, has actually given us far greater freedom. Mighty mechanical and chemical slaves now relieve us of our worst drudgery and really simplify life. Ask the housewife who has done all the work in an unimproved farm house and later moved to a city house, equipped with a gas range, an oil burner, electric refrigerator, electric laundry machines, running water, electric light, telephone, and well-plumbed bath room, which house simplified her life, gave her freedom to gain some degree of culture. As Kettering puts it, "In the old days when the world was simple, life was complex."

Scientific inventions have crowded us together in enormous industrial centers and thus created new social problems, but it must be admitted that many of these social problems are solved by scientific methods. What would life in a great city be like without safe and plentiful city water, modern sewage disposal, electric or gas lighting of streets, modern plumbing, and efficient transportation? In the Middle Ages you could see and be thrilled by a walled city while miles away—and you could also smell it. If today there are any picturesque towns in Europe that smell it is because their citizens are leading the simple life and not making use of modern sanitary engineering.

The poor man today can ride along a smooth road in a bus or a railway train with far greater comfort than belonged to Nero as he bumped along the Appian Way in a springless, solid-tired chariot. His couriers and spies—wires and wireless —bring him news of the outposts of empire with a speed and accuracy that would have made Genghis Khan turn green with envy.

Softer garments clothe the average citizen today, more beautiful colors please him, more warmth and light help him through the winter, better medicines alleviate his sufferings, fresher and more varied foods come to his table, more learning is his for the asking, as results of scientific research.

"There never was a time when any one's efforts for good were so quickly and so generally broadcast. A world calamity on one side of the globe instantly stirs the best feelings in millions of hearts on the other side, and produces generous action before it is too late."

"With the possible exception of music, no form of human activity is so independent of national barriers as scientific research."

Wrong distribution of profits, overproduction, poor use of spare time, challenge us, but these problems will not be solved by calling a moratorium of scientific research for ten years.

"Critics of the Scientific Age again express the fear that the tools of destruction now being produced by the scientist and the engineer will, in the near future, blot out civilization because of their terrible death-dealing possibilities. I have an idea that the first stone axe was viewed with much the same alarm and the invention of gunpowder certainly must have raised the same fears. Yet the race has increased and prospered, protective and defensive measures keeping close pace with destructive tendencies."

"Produce," shouted Carlyle, "if it be but the pitifulest infinitesimal fraction of a product, in God's name, produce."

Grasselli Chemical Co.

FIG. 7. Out of the test tube.

II

NOT OF SUCH STUFF
AS DREAMS ARE MADE

THE CHEMIST deals with a very material world, even though philosophers assure him that he doesn't really know matter, that he only perceives its attributes or properties. However, he is not to be argued out of his dinner by mere words.

Once he has convinced himself that a certain yellow substance or material burns with a blue flame and choking odor, dissolves in liquid carbon disulfide but not in water, melts at a definite temperature and boils at another, combines with iron when hot to form a new substance with its own definite properties, he suspects that sulfur is to blame for all these attacks on his senses.

With enough properties to consider (and there are several more peculiar to sulfur) he feels certain that the source of all these attributes cannot be gold nor, in fact, any other material than what, for lack of a better name, he calls sulfur. If every portion of such a material continues to manifest its existence by exactly the same properties, not merely to one observer, who may be blind or have a cold in the nose or delirium tremens, but to many observers, all doubts are swept aside. The most skeptical chemist now considers it proved that there is something occupying a portion of space and radiating these attacks on his senses. It is voted unanimously to call it sulfur, the same yesterday, today, and tomorrow, a substance.

Yes, it is by such properties, or combinations of them, that we recognize all our known 500,000 different kinds of matter. In other words, there are at least that many different substances. One sniff of hydrogen sulfide, the substance essential to rotten egg odor, and the dullest neophyte in chemistry recognizes it, for no other substance has exactly that convincing odor. True, transparency alone in a solid does not distinguish glass from the other transparent solids but taken in conjunction with degree of hardness and conduct when heated in air the distinction can be made.

We even use conductance of heat and electricity, crystal shape, and index of light refraction, in our detective work.

CHEMICAL LECTURES.

FIG. 8. Professor Friedrich Christian Accum, London chemist, came to be an extremely popular lecturer on chemical subjects about 1802. This cartoon, by T. Rowlandson, appeared in a London publication of the time. It shows Accum giving a chemical lecture before an audience at the Surrey Institution of London. Accum's lectures were printed, and were eagerly read by young and old. In this cartoon, the elderly gentleman in the lower left-hand corner is shown with a copy of "Accum's Lectures" projecting from his coat pocket.

It is for these properties that we value different substances, copper for its great electrical conductivity, lead for its softness and malleability, carborundum for its hardness, rubber for its elasticity, sugar and saccharin for their sweetness.

But the chemist is not a mere detective; he is called upon to separate the sheep from the goats, the chaff from the wheat. Iron ore is of no actual value to mankind until the iron in it is separated, by drastic torture with hot coke, from the oxygen to which it was so closely bound. For that matter sugar has to be separated from the cane to give maximum service, and gold from quartz before it is available for currency.

The preparation of substances is the third great duty of the chemist. For example sulfur is burned to yield a gas, sulfur dioxide, necessary to the bleaching of paper pulp, and sulfur dioxide, in turn, is converted into sulfuric acid, the very foundation of chemical industry. You can actually give your order for the preparation, really the creation, of brand new substances, overlooked by Nature.

Of course change is essential to the preparation of one substance from another and while this chemical change is going on there is always a gain or loss of energy. That is where the physicist gets busy. When Light, Heat, Electricity, or various forms of Motion appear or disappear or are transformed into each other we agree that Physics has a right to the field. But Chemistry and Physics have interlocking interests, as when the chemical energy of coal is converted into heat in a boiler or into motion in the engine or into electricity in the dynamo or into light and heat in the lamp, and finally back into chemical energy, developed in a fern growing under the lamp. Nothing is lost.

Of the appalling host of different substances some are so complex that years of exhausting research have been required to unravel their tangled threads while one hundred and one substances are so simple that they have not been taken apart into simpler substances. These are elementary, well termed elements in distinction from the others, the compounds. We were hard put to it for a bullet-proof definition of an element when the prize element, radium, was actually caught breaking into well-known elementary pieces such as helium and lead. Chemistry teachers then understood just how a hen feels when eggs entrusted to her care hatch out ducklings or turtles. But since no one can hasten or retard this radium breakdown and it is quite extraordinary we apologetically murmur that "an element is a substance that cannot be broken down into simpler substances by ordinary chemical methods." As late as

1808 the world had failed to take quick-lime apart and so considered it an element. Then along came young Sir Humphry Davy and calmly took it apart. Not only that but he repaired Humpty Dumpty by burning the calcium part in oxygen, changing it into a white solid with exactly the same properties as the old lime. Good experiment and sound logic. On the other hand up to 1810 the world, including Lavoisier, spoke of a certain greenish-yellow gas as a compound of hydrochloric acid and oxygen. Again Sir Humphry came to the rescue and, by convincing everybody that the supposed compound could not be taken apart, was allowed to call it an element, chlorine.

It would outrage the truth if we said that most of our one hundred and one elements belong to the *nouveau riche,* for some 92 existed "when the morning stars sang together," but it is a fact that only seventeen were known in Lavoisier's youth, about two hundred years ago. Every new element, when properly introduced by sufficiently distinguished chemists, has been welcomed and much sought after. Priestley, Scheele, Davy, Ramsay, were leaders among the Immortals who discovered elements. Unfortunately for aspiring young candidates for membership in such a world academy, the list of old elements to be discovered is closed. However Seaborg and his associates in California have brilliantly created new elements, heavier than those already existing.

Some of these building blocks of the universe are so rare that the man who has seen all of them is almost as rare. It takes nearly eighty of them to make up one per cent of the earth's crust, while oxygen alone accounts for one-half and silicon for one-fourth of all the material within our reach.

When an eighty-ton meteor was dug out in Africa recently it was found to be a mass of iron and nickel. Even larger visitors from interstellar space have been found. The Peary meteor, which made Greenland its first stopping place and the New York Museum of Natural History its second, weighs thirty-six tons. Although valued at millions of dollars, gangsters are not interested.

ATOMIC WEIGHTS (1954)

	Symbol	Atomic Number	Atomic Weight		Symbol	Atomic Number	Atomic Weight
Actinium	Ac	89	227	Neodymium	Nd	60	144.27
Aluminum	Al	13	26.98	Neptunium	Np	93	[237]
Americium	Am	95	[243]	Neon	Ne	10	20.183
Antimony	Sb	51	121.76	Nickel	Ni	28	58.69
Argon	A	18	39.944	Niobium	Nb	41	92.91
Arsenic	As	33	74.91	(Columbium)			
Astatine	At	85	[210]	Nitrogen	N	7	14.008
Barium	Ba	56	137.36	Osmium	Os	76	190.2
Berkelium	Bk	97	[245]	Oxygen	O	8	16.000
Beryllium	Be	4	9.013	Palladium	Pd	46	106.7
Bismuth	Bi	83	209.00	Phosphorus	P	15	30.975
Boron	B	5	10.82	Platinum	Pt	78	195.23
Bromine	Br	35	79.916	Plutonium	Pu	94	[242]
Cadmium	Cd	48	112.41	Polonium	Po	84	210
Calcium	Ca	20	40.08	Potassium	K	19	39.10
Californium	Cf	98	[248]	Praseodymium	Pr	59	140.92
Carbon	C	6	12.011	Promethium	Pm	61	[145]
Cerium	Ce	58	140.13	Protactinium	Pa	91	231
Cesium	Cs	55	132.91	Radium	Ra	88	226.05
Chlorine	Cl	17	35.457	Radon	Rn	86	222
Chromium	Cr	24	52.01	Rhenium	Re	75	186.31
Cobalt	Co	27	58.94	Rhodium	Rh	45	102.91
Copper	Cu	29	63.54	Rubidium	Rb	37	85.48
Curium	Cm	96	[245]	Ruthenium	Ru	44	101.1
Dysprosium	Dy	66	162.46	Samarium	Sm	62	150.43
Erbium	Er	68	167.2	Scandium	Sc	21	44.96
Europium	Eu	63	152.0	Selenium	Se	34	78.96
Fluorine	Fl	9	19.00	Silicon	Si	14	28.09
Francium	Fr	87	[223]	Silver	Ag	47	107.880
Gadolinium	Gd	64	156.9	Sodium	Na	11	22.991
Gallium	Ga	31	69.72	Strontium	Sr	38	87.63
Germanium	Ge	32	72.60	Sulfur	S	16	32.066
Gold	Au	79	197.0	Tantalum	Ta	73	180.95
Hafnium	Hf	72	178.6	Technetium	Tc	43	[99]
Helium	He	2	4.003	Tellurium	Te	52	127.61
Holmium	Ho	67	164.94	Terbium	Tb	65	158.93
Hydrogen	H	1	1.0080	Thallium	Tl	81	204.39
Indium	In	49	114.76	Thorium	Th	90	232.05
Iodine	I	53	126.91	Thulium	Tm	69	168.94
Iridium	Ir	77	192.2	Tin	Sn	50	118.70
Iron	Fe	26	55.85	Titanium	Ti	22	47.90
Krypton	Kr	36	83.80	Tungsten	W	74	183.92
Lanthanum	La	57	138.92	Uranium	U	92	238.07
Lead	Pb	82	207.21	Vanadium	V	23	50.95
Lithium	Li	3	6.940	Xenon	Xe	54	131.3
Lutetium	Lu	71	174.99	Ytterbium	Yb	70	173.04
Magnesium	Mg	12	24.32	Yttrium	Y	39	88.92
Manganese	Mn	25	54.94	Zinc	Zn	30	65.38
Mercury	Hg	80	200.61	Zirconium	Zr	40	91.22
Molybdenum	Mo	42	95.95				

Experience has taught us to be cautious in calling any element useless. That was what we thought of neon when Sir William Ramsay discovered this lazy gas in the air, one part in eighty thousand, yet today the neon-filled lamps or lighting tubes along the shopping district tell all but the blind where to eat or where to buy shoes. Tungsten remained a long time on the museum shelves yet now it is called one of the five key metals of industry.

It is very difficult to find another element but you may win a crown, golden at that, by discovering good uses for those elements remaining uncalled for. There is tellurium, for example, lying in huge refuse heaps from Colorado mines that were dug for gold, silver, and lead. It is also a by-product in copper refining. Since a trace in the diet confers on the breath the odor of rotten horseradish, an inventive public health officer proposed that victims of contagious diseases should be given tellurium pills as an effective method of isolation. Up to date this doctor has not been listed in Dun and Bradstreet.

When it concerns our own personal machine, the human body, a very little of some of the elements is quite enough, but leave them out entirely and the machine fails to function. Just 0.004 of one per cent is our quota of iron, a vital constituent of the red hemoglobin of the blood, the means of carrying oxygen from lungs to remotest tissue. Curiously enough in the oyster, lobster, and their kin, copper seems to replace iron as the respiratory pigment of the blood. The significance of iron in building up the green chlorophyll of leaves, though not itself a part of this pigment, is dramatically stated by Gortner. "If nature were to forget for a single year, perhaps less, the secret formula for the synthesis of chlorophyll, it is highly probable that all the mammals and perhaps all the other forms of life, with the exception of certain bacteria and fungi, would be annihilated. Chlorophyll cannot be synthesized in the plant if iron is absent!"

An average man has sometimes been contemptuously referred to as nothing but twelve pounds of ashes and eight buckets of water. There is a grain or two of truth in the jibe, but the science of medicine longs for complete knowledge of the way most of that water is held. For example, Gortner informs us that "the brain, isolated from the body, can swell with water one thousand per cent and still maintain its coherence. If it swells three per cent during life, coma and death ensue."

Evidently the mystery of life is not explained by a mere chemical analysis of the human body.

III

WITH FIRE MAN ROSE
ABOVE THE BEASTS

WITHOUT FIRE man would still be eating his meat raw, living in caves or in the crudest of structures, depending upon mere muscle power or rough-hewn wooden water wheels and wind-mills, driven to darkness by set of sun, still living in the Stone Age.

Fire has lengthened the day, driven away fierce beasts, brought warmth and comfort, cooked tough foods, ushered in the Bronze Age, the Iron Age, the Age of Mechanical Power. In the light of such benefits from an old servant is it any wonder that the ancients credited Prometheus with the theft of fire from Heaven or that, in rueful consideration of its cruelty as a master, they also placed it in Hell? The Parsees of Persia worshiped the flame and burned jets of natural gas for centuries; the Vestal Virgins tended the eternal fire in ancient Rome; everywhere it was a part of religious ritual.

How astonishing that with ages of cautious familiarity with fire it was never really understood until a century and a half ago. Throughout the eighteenth century able scientists sought to explain the burning of wood as an escape of a mysterious spirit called Phlogiston. The upward rush of flame did give some such impression and it was natural for them to explain the failure of the ash to burn further by the simple statement that it had lost all of its phlogiston. Unfortunately for such logic Jean Rey (1630), Lomonossov, and Lavoisier each "calcined" lead and tin, that is, heated these metals in air, with careful weighing of both metal and ash. The ash weighed more instead of less, as with wood. This made the phlogistonists squirm until one adroit squirmer invented the conception of negative gravity for phlogiston, never thinking that such a quality only made matters worse in the case of the wood fire.

The final explanation of burning or combustion was achieved by Lavoisier in Paris with his great mercury experiment. With admirable—and most profitable—patience he heated mercury in a retort partly filled with air, for twelve days, and was rewarded by the slow appearance of a red powder on the surface of the mercury. The open end of the retort dipped under a dish of water, so rise of water in

Fig. 9. No wonder the Neanderthal man worshiped fire.

the vessel indicated contraction in volume of the enclosed air or a disappearance of some part of this air. Like a good experimenter, Lavoisier continued his heating until there was no further loss in volume of the air resting on the hot mercury and then noted that one fifth of the air had disappeared. A splinter failed to burn in what remained of the air. With painstaking care he removed the precious red powder and heated it much hotter in another tube. To his intense delight the gas released from the red powder exactly equaled in volume the loss in volume of the air previously heated in contact with mercury. His conclusion, which you have already anticipated by this time, was that hot mercury united with some unknown element in the air to form the red compound of mercury with this element. At higher temperatures this compound was decomposed, liberating the mysterious element.

Now Priestley, the political-minded English clergyman,

had just visited Lavoisier and described the "good air" or active gas that he obtained by heating (with a great sun lens) some red "mercurous calcinatus." In this gas glowing splinters burst into flame and mice frisked about more actively than in air. Very good air indeed, almost the essence of air.

Putting two and two together Lavoisier quickly named the element that Priestley had discovered, "oxygen," and announced that it is the essential component of air, one fifth in volume, with which metals unite to form an ash such as the red oxide of mercury, or with which wood unites in the process of burning. At last the mystery of fire was cleared up.

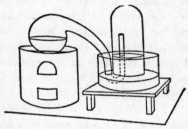

FIG. 10. With this apparatus Lavoisier discovered the real meaning of combustion.

Thanks to Priestley in 1774 and to Scheele, working independently in Sweden, science was enriched with a new element, oxygen, the greatest and most plentiful of all. Air, water, rocks, clays, plants, and animals owe about half of their weight to an element not recognized until 1774.

A naïve freshman once asked what people breathed before oxygen was discovered! It is actually the breath of life to all animals, needed to "burn up" waste tissue. The body is a sort of furnace, stoked with food and a forced draft of air, yielding practically the same amount of heat as if the foods were burned in a calorimeter, or a heat-measuring furnace. Just as carbon dioxide and water vapor are the chief products of the burning of wood so are they important constituents of the air exhaled from our lungs. The chemical energy of food is converted into motion of muscles and into bodily heat.

During violent exertion we must get our energy by a short-cut from glycogen, a starch-like substance found in reserve in the liver. "When muscle tissue contracts and does work it derives the necessary free energy, not from oxidation, which is not quick enough, but from the rapid exothermic conversion of the carbohydrate, glycogen, into lactic acid. When the fatigued muscle recovers, it recharges its store of free energy; that is to say by oxidizing or burning some of the carbohydrate, it reconverts the lactic acid into glycogen. . . . The story of this mode of action and recovery of the muscle cells forms one of the most fascinating chapters of modern science." (*Donnan.*)

A few years ago while A. V. Hill of London was guest professor at Cornell University, he created quite a flurry of interest on the athletic fields by enlisting athletes in his study of the chemistry of exhaustion. Brain and brawn cooperated; mighty halfbacks wheeled loads of brick, with huge breathing bags upon their backs; fast sprinters did the 100 yard dash under close chemical check; all in the cause of simple honesty. It appeared that a fast dash man breathes in only about one eighth of the oxygen needed during his 100 yard dash—he goes into debt for oxygen and later pays that debt by much rapid breathing during a prolonged rest. The thirty grams (about one ounce) of lactic acid developed in ten seconds of such tremendous effort made him tired, yet, given time to breathe in enough extra oxygen to convert the thirty grams of this acid of sour milk back into readily available glycogen, the honest young sprinter paid off his oxygen debt. In a long race a runner owing the world fifteen liters (about four gallons) of oxygen is staggering, completely exhausted.

Oxygen has become a recognized ally of the physician who puts a tent over the head of a patient too weak to breathe his quota and, by enriching the air with this vital gas, saves the weakened patient much exertion. Even high-flying pilots need cylinders of oxygen.

When the early dentists used laughing gas, nitrous oxide, as an anesthetic a few martyrs probably lost teeth and life as well. They merely choked to death. By bitter experience we learned to mix oxygen with laughing gas. The aviator, skimming along the sky ceiling, carries a strong cylinder of compressed oxygen to keep himself conscious.

Yet we can have too much of a good thing. If the atmosphere were all oxygen we should be as badly off as King Midas with his diet of solid gold. In the first place the nitrogen, some four fifths in volume, is more than a filler or diluent —it is the ultimate source of the nitrogen in animal and plant protein. In the second place the carbon dioxide of the air is vital to plant life. In the third place, without water vapor in the air there would be no rain, therefore nothing but oceans and a parched land. In the fourth place our body mechanism couldn't stand the pace and the furnace fire would, perhaps, burn out the grate bars.

We call union of oxygen with some other substance **oxidation** (though there is a broader definition now) and an oxidation violent enough to give off light and heat, **combustion.** Iron rusts or is oxidized in moist air, but a bit of steel picture wire actually burns brilliantly in a jar of pure oxygen.

Combustible dusts with their great surface permit more rapid oxidation because the air touches every particle. "Pyrophoric iron," an extraordinarily dusty form of iron, ignites spontaneously when tossed into the air. And when it comes to fine dusts of starch, flour, coal, cocoa, sugar, fertilizers, sulfur, alfalfa, soap, and leather suspended in the air of factories we must, on peril of life itself, avoid flames or sparks. The almost instantaneous burning of such combustible material and consequent explosive formation of great volumes of gases has cost us scores of lives and many millions of dollars in a single year.

"Spontaneous combustion" in coal piles, in rags or waste soaked with fatty oils, or in haymows, is common enough to be serious. Soft coal stored in huge heaps is oxidized slowly but when the temperature rises 10° Centigrade (about 18° Fahrenheit) the speed of this reaction is doubled, in fact it is approximately doubled for every 10° rise, like all reaction velocities. Of course with free air circulation or ventilation this heat is conducted away readily and the rate of oxidation remains very slow. In huge piles, however, the conditions may be favorable for actual flame.

The economic and sociological features of the soft coal industry are closely interwoven with this storage loss of the fuel. Steady production throughout the entire year is desirable but not profitable for the mine-owner.

Oxygen concerns us in other ways, less apparent. Paint, for example, never really "dries" for it has no water to lose.

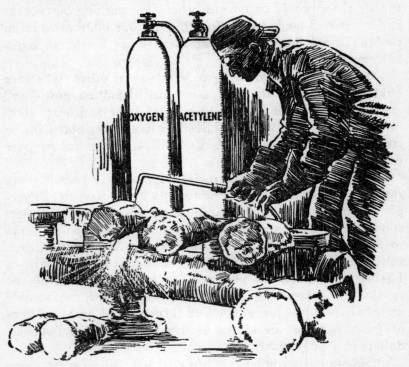

FIG. 11. The oxy-acetylene flame cuts massive scrap steel more easily than a saw cuts wood.

The linseed oil present merely unites with oxygen to form a tough, solid compound.

If you are minded now to vote for oxygen as the central element of this chemical world you can probably carry the election by feeding the fish ballots for bait. Fish have more than an academic interest in the fact that oxygen dissolves slightly but distinctly in water. They cannot breathe air but with their gills they can pick up this dissolved oxygen for their blood. If our own very remote ancestors took to the water before they took to the trees they, too, may have had gills. But it is to be feared at this point that a gill-less chemist is getting beyond his depth.

Iron and oxygen are both friends and enemies. The final end of all this iron and steel framework of the age is rust, an iron oxide. But rusty old bridges and locomotives are cut up into pieces convenient for shipment back to the steel mill— cut up by the intense heat of a torch fed with pure oxygen and hydrogen or other good fuel. The operation is somewhat suggestive of the progress of a hot knife through cold butter. To give these oxygen-fed torches their due we must observe that they are invaluable as welding tools. At the steel mill this steel "scrap" is fed into open-hearth furnaces, robbed of its oxygen, and poured out as excellent molten metal, ready to start on a new career. The original source of all iron is the ore, usually an oxide. Although the stealing of this combined oxygen and liberation of the metal from the ore is accomplished by the burning of coke mixed with the ore, it could all be done far more readily if pure oxygen, or even an air richer than usual in oxygen, could be blown into the base of the stack.

Hence the demand for cheaper sources of pure oxygen. At present most of it is made by liquefying air (with great pressure and cooling), allowing the more volatile nitrogen to evaporate first and saving the residual liquid as pretty good oxygen. Of course it must be kept or shipped in huge thermos bottles or in powerful steel cylinders.

Steel cylinders of compressed oxygen are life-savers for patients too weak to inhale enough air, to aviators in the stratosphere, and to the crews of submarines.

As a sort of postscript to this chapter, ozone might at least be mentioned. This is the source of the pungent odor observed around flying belts and frictional electrical machines. Electric discharges of various sorts, even the lightning flash and, most of all, the ultra-violet rays of the sun, change common oxygen into the more active form of ozone—and then the ozone changes back or wears its life away oxidizing bacteria, dirt, and the like. When you swell out your chest on a cold, snappy winter's day and urge your friends to "smell the ozone" there may be more truth than humor in your words. It is only in the upper air that the solar ultra-violet light is intense enough to change an appreciable amount of oxygen into ozone. Whirling mountains of air called by the weather man "high barometric areas" sometimes roll down to the earth some of this upper ozone before the dust, moisture and heat of the lower air can ruin it.

We are now assured that we sleep more warmly because of an extra blanket of ozone a few miles above our beds, a blanket that checks the loss of the earth's heat radiations.

It is all very well a few miles up, but any more than enough to make you wonder if you are really smelling it is too much, is too irritating for daily life down here. Ozonized air has been made in electric machines equipped with fans, and used to kill (or oxidize) odors in storage warehouses, kitchens, and even London's "tupenny tubes." There were suggestions that a little ozone be introduced into Parliament to perk up the sleepy or merely bored members, and many were the college professors who toyed with the thought of reinforcing teaching with a touch of ozone.

This ozone blanket, about twenty-five miles above us, amounts to enough to make a layer only two millimeters thick if pure, yet its ability to stop the passage of excessive ultra-violet light protects us from sunstroke in summer.*

* Holmes, Harry N. "Atmospheric Ozone." *American Chemical Journal*, pp. 47, 497, 1912.

IV

THE IMPORTANCE OF NOTHING AT ALL

THE NEAREST we can get to nothing on this planet is the modern high vacuum and yet a cubic inch of the best vacuum is densely populated with more molecules of gas than there are people on the earth, with 40,000,000,000 to be exact. And at that, only one ten-billionth of the original gas is left, thanks to Langmuir's mercury vapor pump.

"If from a vessel holding a quart there were removed one million molecules a second, it would take 750,000,000 years to remove practically all of its air, but the Langmuir pump accomplishes this in just two seconds." Even so, our highest vacua are quite dense as compared to some of the distant stars, "incandescent masses of nothing at all."

High vacua, or even partial vacua, minister to our comfort and serve us well in many ways. They made possible the original incandescent lamp (although the type has since changed), the X-ray tube, the radio bulb, the photoelectric cell of sound pictures, the thermos bottle, suction pumps, and they increase the efficiency of steam engines and turbines.

The color effects accompanying electrical discharges in rarefied gases have made possible the cheap but ghostly light from the mercury vapor lamps much used in factories, and the beautiful pink glow of the neon tubes used for advertising signs. Probably the magnificent effects of the aurora borealis are due to similar discharges through the highly attenuated atmosphere a hundred miles above us.

And so it appears that, by the vital aid of practically nothing at all, the vision of physicians and surgeons is so extended that human suffering is alleviated through correct diagnosis; cancerous growths are in some measure controlled; curative summer sunshine is available in the darkest days of winter; the electric lighting of homes was made possible; the actual voice of speaker or orchestra is heard without effort by countless millions; the "electrical eye," like an educated robot, controls factory operations; and hot food is kept hot and cold drinks cold, for lunch or picnic.

Since a good vacuum is not much more than a ghost of a gas our attention might well be led on to the merits of gas in robust health, possibly even bursting with health.

Nearly three centuries ago Robert Boyle toyed with an air pump and made the startling discovery that air has a "spring" to it. And he found that if he worked his pump

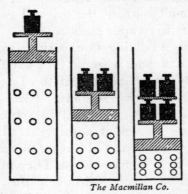

The Macmillan Co.

Fig. 12. The volume occupied by a given number of molecules of a gas varies inversely as the pressure.

hard enough he could push into a strong bottle an astonishing lot of air. If poor Boyle hadn't lived so far ahead of his time he would probably have invented pneumatic tires for automobiles. But he did discover the fact that by doubling the weight on a movable plunger in a cylinder of air or other gas the plunger sank half the remaining distance or, in other words, with doubled pressure on a definite weight of gas the volume occupied was halved. All scientists now speak respectfully of Boyle's Law, that "the volume of a gas varies inversely as the pressure."

Later the great Gay-Lussac, and Charles, too, observed that gases, like invalids, shrink from the cold; shrink 1/273 of their volume if cooled a single degree Centigrade. It was a somewhat humorous speculation that if any particular volume of any gas was cooled from 0° C. on down some 273°, the entire volume, 273/273 of it, would be charged off to shrinkage in value. There wouldn't be any gas left. This would be destruction of matter, and our experience teaches us that matter always reappears somewhere in some form after brutal treatment. Furthermore, gases are always cooled to liquids long before the temperature reaches —273° C. Still it is a pleasant thought to dally with, that of this imaginary point of —273° C. where the molecules of a perfect gas quit kicking. So pleased were we with the idea that we called that never-to-be-attained end of the temperature rainbow, **absolute zero,** the place of no molecular motion.

Perhaps it was a bit rash to intimate that there was no hope of reaching absolute zero for Keesom at the University of Leyden liquefied helium and finally froze it to a solid (the first time in history) at a temperature within less than a single degree of this ultimate zero. This was a triumph for up to July, 1926, every known substance except helium had been solidified. Keesom crossed the last frontier in that direction. In 1932 he claimed a temperature only 0.71° above absolute zero, but even this record was broken by Giauque and Mac-Dougall at the University of California with the astonishing temperature of 0.25° absolute.

In 1935 De Haas at Leyden secured a new low temperature, only 0.0044° above Absolute Zero. The final stage depended upon the remarkable fact that the magnetization of certain paramagnetic salts such as cerium fluoride produces a rise in temperature (which heat could be removed), while demagnetization following this step produces a lowering of temperature. Repetition of these steps led to the final triumph.

Mere pressure in crowding together the molecules of a gas does not always succeed in producing a liquid, so scientists, about a century ago, gave up five gases in despair of ever overcoming their repugnance to the liquid state. Then came a common sense application of the observations of both Boyle and Charles that gases could best be compressed with the aid of cooling and pressure together. We must cool hydrogen, one of the obstinate gases, at least to —234° C. or even the most tremendous pressures fail to liquefy it. Below this critical temperature all is well. At —259° C. liquid hydrogen freezes to a transparent ice-like solid, the lightest solid in existence.

All this struggle to compress gases, the enormous decrease in their volume when liquefied, and their exertion of pressure in all directions as shown in a tight football will convince us that in gases the molecules are relatively far apart, in ordinary air about a dozen times their own diameter, and that they are in violent motion, rebounding from each other with perfect elasticity. If they lost any energy in a collision the old gases certainly would be asleep by this time. At 20° C. (room temperature) a single hydrogen molecule (H_2) collides with its fellows ten million times a second.

Think of the life led by a poor inflated football! Even on a freezing day its walls are

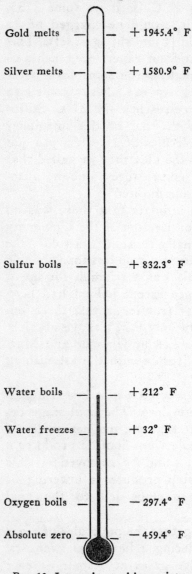

Gold melts — + 1945.4° F

Silver melts — + 1580.9° F

Sulfur boils — + 832.3° F

Water boils — + 212° F

Water freezes — + 32° F

Oxygen boils — — 297.4° F

Absolute zero — — 459.4° F

FIG. 13. Interesting melting points and boiling points.

pounded with a merciless hailstorm of molecules moving a quarter of a mile per second. No wonder it swells up after an extra dose of molecules has been forced inside. And it swells still more if brought into a warm room. The speed of the flying molecules is increased.

The business of selling highly compressed or liquefied gases is no infant industry. In a recent year such products in this country alone were valued at $500,000,000. Three billion cubic feet of compressed oxygen, one billion cubic feet of acetylene, and enormous volumes of ammonia (not the water solution), carbon dioxide, chlorine, nitrous oxide, butane, and hydrogen make an astonishing total.

The transition from gas to liquid is quite familiar to us in the change from steam to ordinary water as is the opposing change of liquid to gas in the teakettle or steam boiler.

Liquid ⇄ Gas

In the liquid the molecules are packed so closely that their mutual attraction maintains the liquid state, unless somebody increases their nervous agitation, in other words, raises the temperature. Then the molecules on the surface hoist anchor and fly away as a vapor, they evaporate. With common ether, a very volatile substance, this is quite noticeable. Water boils when the rise of temperature produces such an outward, or upward, pressure of escaping water vapor that the downward pressure of the air is barely exceeded—at exactly 100° C. or 212° F. at sea level; at lower temperatures on mountain tops. Each liquid has its own boiling point, a fact well known in the art of distillation.

The concentration of the weak fermented liquors to yield 45 per cent whiskey, through distillation, is far from being the only use of our knowledge of distillation but it is an interesting example. It might be imagined that on raising the temperature of a mixture of alcohol, with a boiling point of 78° C., and water with a boiling point of 100° C., all the alcohol would distil over at exactly 78°. Far from it. Some alcohol escapes, it is true, but it rushes some water vapor along with it. It might also be thought that at 100 C. only water would pass over. Another mistake. Somehow the liquid water holds back much alcohol that should have escaped at 78° and so the distillate at 100° C. contains a small percentage of alcohol.

The commercial distiller uses a "column still," and so does the oil refiner, a device by which the more-readily condensed vapors in a mixture are continually condensed and drained back into the boiling mixture while only the more volatile vapors "turn the corner" at the top of this vertical column and condense as "distillate." Chemical industry in general profits greatly by this device.

Just as heat is given off in a household radiator during the change from steam to liquid water, fortunately for your comfort, so must heat be absorbed from surrounding bodies when a liquid evaporates. Note the cooling produced when ether evaporates from a pool held in the palm of your hand. Surgeons fear to use ether as an anesthetic for patients already threatened with pneumonia. The very considerable cooling of the lungs caused by evaporation of the ether is sometimes just enough to cause pneumonia complications.

Quite similar is the underlying principle of the great refrigeration industry, with all its comforts, its prolongation of the season for fresh foods, its contribution to health on board ship, and its extension of the market highways. Ammonia, or Freon for domestic use, is compressed, the heat of compression removed by a stream of water or a current of air, and the compressed gas allowed to expand. The expansion absorbs heat from the cooling coils, produces refrigeration. The cycle is repeated endlessly. Since the power for compression comes, perhaps, from coal it is only a seeming paradox to say that we cool the brine in the coils of pipe with a lump of coal. There are many variations in refrigerating processes, some even operating without motor compressor.

On a warship carbon dioxide is a safer refrigerant than

either ammonia or sulfur dioxide due to the danger of damage from a well-placed shell.

A peculiar industry has developed recently in connection with carbon dioxide. When this gas is allowed to expand it cools so rapidly that it freezes itself to snow. This snow, or "dry ice," is compressed into cakes and used in shipping ice cream, meats, etc. Since it evaporates into a harmless gas, perfectly dry, it has distinct advantages over ice, although necessarily more expensive. We use 400,000 tons annually.

TEMPERATURE EXTREMES

Absolute zero	$-459.4°$ F.
Lowest temperature reached	$-459.3919°$ F.
Liquid air boils at about	$-296°$ F.
Coldest Siberian weather	$-90°$ F.
Hottest weather, Tripoli	$+136°$ F.
Best electric furnace	$+4,900°$ F.
Oxy-acetylene torch	$+5,500°$ F.
Atomic hydrogen flame	$+7,640°$ F.
Exploding electric wire (record)	$+45,000°$ F.
Center of giant stars	$+72,000,000°$ F.

V

LANGUAGE AND TOOLS

THE QUANTITATIVE studies of materials during chemical change, initiated by Joseph Black of England in 1755, paved the way for the atomic theory, in fact made it inevitable.

For example, when iron filings and sulfur are heated together a new product is formed with very different properties from either iron or sulfur, a product called ferrous sulfide. If you tried the experiments repeatedly with hit-or-miss proportions of iron and sulfur you might be able to pull out some of the iron with a magnet from one product or dissolve out part of the sulfur by the aid of the right liquid in another, and in still another find it impossible to remove either sulfur or iron.

By weighing everything concerned you would learn that the two elements always unite in a very exact proportion. When more iron than this in relation to the sulfur is used that much iron is left over, removable by a magnet; when more sulfur is taken than exactly enough to combine with the iron present this excess of sulfur is left over, removable by washing with a good solvent for free sulfur.

Evidently this ferrous sulfide, when freed from other materials, has an exact or definite composition. So true is this of all pure substances that we even speak of the Law of Definite Composition. Cooks may create a delicious cake with a "pinch of this and a little of that" but they cannot tinker with a pure chemical substance that way. Just so much carbon unites, in burning, with just so much oxygen to form carbon dioxide. But go slowly there. When there is too much hot carbon for the oxygen supplied, a very poisonous gas results, carbon monoxide by name. However, that is a very different substance from carbon dioxide and no chemist can vary its composition at will. If he could it should be possible to mix carbon and oxygen in an infinite number of different proportions and thus produce countless oxides of carbon. No, it will be one of the two with, possibly, an excess of carbon or oxygen to remove. You can't fool Nature; she knows her two oxides of carbon.

A little more than a century ago this marvelous exactness of reaction proportions worried an English teacher named John Dalton. He decided that if matter, especially of elementary substances, were absolutely continuous there could be no exact or definite proportions in reaction. A little more iron or a trifle less might just as well unite with a fixed weight of sulfur, for example.

So Dalton came to the conclusion that matter is made up of minute pellets (or atoms), and that definite numbers of these unite in reactions. His atomic theory stated further that:

1. The ultimate particles of a pure substance, simple or compound, are alike in size or weight;
2. The "simple atoms" of an elementary substance are indivisible, and can neither be created nor destroyed;
3. The "compound atoms" of a chemical compound are formed by the union of two or more elementary atoms;
4. Combination between atoms takes place in the simplest possible ratios, e.g., one atom of A with one, two, or three atoms of B.

How convenient to use the term molecule for the smallest compound particle formed by the union of two or more atoms of different kinds! A chemical reaction, then, is merely a regrouping of atoms in new combinations and the atom is the smallest particle of an element taking part in chemical reactions. There is no law against two or three atoms of the same kind grouping together in molecules of an elementary substance. That is exactly the difference between common oxygen and ozone. Two atoms of oxygen move about in little groups, or molecules, as common oxygen gas, and yet if shaken up by the drastic action of silent electric discharge, some groupings of atoms in threes are observed—ozone appears.

This theory fits perfectly into the facts. A single atom of

carbon may unite with either one or two atoms of oxygen to form carbon monoxide or carbon dioxide, but if these atoms are considered indivisible how can one atom of carbon unite with about 1.7354621 atoms of oxygen, for example? Impossible!

For a hundred years, nearly, this theory was remarkably effective as a basis for chemical work, yet without absolute proof of its correctness until the facts of radioactivity were discovered. This theory was not wrong but even a wrong theory may be of real service until the truth is discovered. As some one wrote, why refuse to use a jar or vase while we are developing the science of ceramics?

The existence of molecules is certainly not to be proved by seeing them, for 40,000,000 of them in a row would barely span one inch. So small are they that a census of the molecules contained in a thimble of air would occupy every citizen of the United States for thousands of years. Even so, Millikan states the number in a single cubic centimeter (a thimble holds about 3cc.) as 2.71×10^{19}. If you are skeptical remember that several scientists using a dozen different methods arrived at almost exactly the same figures, nineteen ciphers and all. It is asserted that with every breath you take in a few molecules of air once breathed by imperial Cæsar in the days of Rome's greatest glory.

A preliminary word or two on the modern conception of the atom will not be out of place here although much more along that line will appear in a later chapter.

In high vacuum tubes, now glorified as X-ray tubes, the passage of a high-voltage current of electricity through the rarefied gas is evidenced by peculiar radiations or "cathode rays" streaming from the cathode in straight lines and causing a fluorescence of the glass or other substances in their path. In fact the copper or tungsten "target" interposed in a powerful X-ray tube may be pounded into incandescence by these rays. Since a magnet or an electric field deflects these rays (with effects quite visible in a darkened room) it was easily determined that they are streams of negatively charged particles of some kind. Changing the cathode from platinum to gold or other solids makes no difference nor does changing the rarefied gas—the same streams of the same negatively charged particles are observed. Consequently these **electrons,** as we now call them, are constituents of every kind of atom. This was shown in 1897 by J. J. Thomson and supplemented by Rutherford's discovery of the **proton** or positively charged building block of atoms.

FIG. 14. Oratory alone could not solve the perplexing problem of the constitution of matter.

In rapid succession came various convincing proofs that each atom is made up of an equal number of negative electrons of negligible weight and of positive protons, relatively heavy, with one or more neutral particles (neutrons) of proton weight; that the atom is a miniature solar system, mostly space, with all the protons and neutrons concentrated in an incredibly minute fraction of the atomic space at the center (the nucleus) and with planetary electrons rotating at dizzying speeds, possibly 150,000 miles per second, around the nucleus. Occasionally one or more electrons in an outer orbit fly off to some other inviting atom. Then the atom that loses electrons (negative) is left positive because of its excess of positive charges while the other atom naturally becomes negative. These oppositely charged atoms now attract each other, are wedded as a new substance. This is one type of chemical reaction, but there is another type in which two atoms agree to share pairs of outer electrons and thus hold together in a new molecule, much as door and frame are held together by sharing hinges.

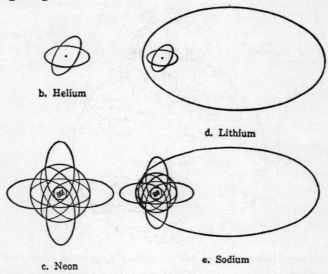

b. Helium

d. Lithium

c. Neon

e. Sodium

FIG. 15. Planetary electrons revolving around the nucleus in different atoms.

The hydrogen atom is very simple for its little solar system is pictured as one electron chasing itself around one proton. Uranium is far more complicated, with 92 electrons, 92 protons and 146 neutrons. It could afford to toss away quite a few protons and electrons, in fact it does that very thing as we shall see in the chapter on radium.

Yes, the modern atom is mostly space with a diameter 100,000 times its own nucleus in the case of gold. If ordinary matter were as compact as the little nucleus life would be ludicrous. The nearest approach to such density is found in a companion to the star Sirius, one cubic inch of which would weigh a ton on our planet.

The public choked a bit at first on this electron theory, but with the advent of radio every lad is ready to inform you that electrons, thrown off by the "hot filament" of the tube,

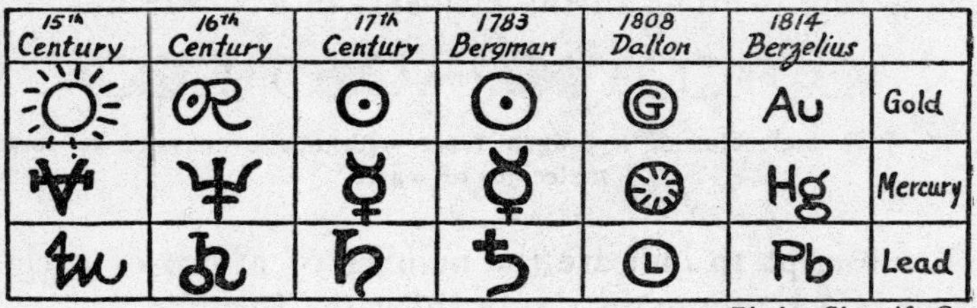

15th Century	16th Century	17th Century	1783 Bergman	1808 Dalton	1814 Berzelius	
☀	♃	☉	☉	Ⓖ	Au	Gold
♅	♆	☿	☿	✳	Hg	Mercury
♃	♄	♄	♄	Ⓛ	Pb	Lead

Fischer Sicentific Co.

FIG. 16. Alchemistic symbols.

are necessary to radio operation. A hot wire anywhere throws off electrons and makes the air near it conduct electricity.

. . .

The early alchemists were a secretive lot, proficient in concealing their findings. Naturally they indulged in mysterious language and used strange symbols for elements and compounds, symbols almost as hard to read as the druggist's prescriptions of today.

At one stroke the great Swedish chemist, Berzelius, replaced this cumbersome nonsense with a nomenclature of logical simplicity. At his suggestion chemists agreed to represent each element by the first letter or two of its Latin name. Thus

Ca	for calcium
C	for carbon
Ag	for silver (from the Latin argentum)
Pb	for lead (from the Latin plumbum)
Fe	for iron (from the Latin ferrum)
K	for potassium (from the Latin kalium)
Na	for sodium (from the Latin natrium)

It has become a matter of convenience to let the symbol represent a single atom of the element.

Just as we represent an individual by writing down all of his names, such as Henry Tutweiler Smith, so we represent a compound by writing down the names of all its elements. To save time we often refer to the gentleman mentioned above as H. T. Smith. Similarly we save time by setting down the symbols representing all the elements in a substance, using a

FIG. 17. Two molecules of hydrogen react with one of oxygen to form two molecules of water.

small subscript to indicate the number of atoms of each sort present in a single molecule, in short the **formula**.

For example the formula H_2O representing water tells the world that in every molecule there are two atoms of hydrogen and one atom of oxygen. A more complicated formula, H_2SO_4, representing sulfuric acid, flashes the news that each molecule contains two atoms of hydrogen, one atom of sulfur and four atoms of oxygen.

FIG. 18. Is sulfuric acid really H_2SO_4?

With the aid of such a shorthand system it is a simple matter to describe in brief for chemists of all races what happens when hydrochloric acid, HCl, is poured on quicklime, CaO.

$$CaO + 2HCl \rightarrow CaCl_2 + H_2O.$$

No one could guess what the products of this reaction might be unless he had experience of his own or of others, to guide him. Somebody must have examined the products and found calcium chloride, $CaCl_2$, present. It is not difficult to recognize by a few of its properties. The reaction represented by the "equation" above tells us what substances are mixed, how many molecules react, what products, and how many molecules of them are formed. The 2HCl represents two molecules of hydrochloric acid while the mere formula CaO represents only one molecule of calcium oxide or quicklime.

Suppose we try another "equation," representing the gas fire in the kitchen range, that is if natural gas, methane, CH_4, is the fuel.

$$CH_4 + 2O_2 \rightarrow CO_2 + 2H_2O.$$

You must take our word for it that there are two atoms of oxygen in a single molecule of oxygen gas. Then the equation above informs us that some chemist has caught and analyzed the gaseous products in the flame, knows them to be water, H_2O, and carbon dioxide, CO_2. Furthermore he must have measured the natural gas, the air used, and the two products in order to be able to set down the relative numbers of molecules concerned.

Beginning chemists sometimes ask despairingly, "How can we be expected to know what is formed in a reaction?" The simple answer is that they cannot know without testing the products, or reading in a book the findings of some chemist who did. We do expect of students, however, that they know the correct formula of a substance named, or know where to find it. Sometimes a confused freshman sets down some such incorrect formula as $CaSO_5$ to represent burnt gypsum ($CaSO_4$). He could be reminded that it is almost sacrilegious and certainly rather late in the day to attempt to change the composition of a substance created ages ago.

There was no Divine Revelation through a chemical Moses giving us these correct formulas. That came from analysis of compounds for their elements, and very exact weighing as well as upon a knowledge of the relative weights of atoms. Lacking the knowledge that human skin is a mixture of substances, a chemist in 1844 analyzed it and announced its formula as $C_{40}H_{66}N_{12}O_{15}S$.

"When you can measure what you are speaking about and express it in numbers, you know something about it, and when you cannot measure it, when you cannot express it in numbers, your knowledge is of a very meager and unsatisfactory kind. It may be the beginning of knowledge, but you have scarcely, in your thought, advanced to the stage of a science." (*Lord Kelvin.*)

Evidently the chemist is required to do some accurate measuring. He uses the units of the international metric system, and saves much time. Think of a system relating units of length, volume and weight so closely that a cube of water ten centimeters (about four inches) along an edge, containing 1000 cubic centimeters or one liter, weighs 1000 grams or one kilogram. No such simple relations hold for our stupid and expensive English system of weights and measures. The metric system is a decimal system throughout, while that in general

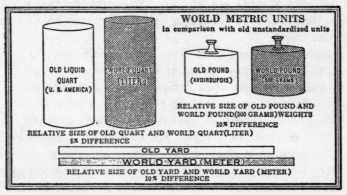

FIG. 19. The Metric System is quickly learned.

public use in English-speaking countries becomes decimal only in counting American money. No, that is not quite fair, for our machinist, bitterly opposing adoption of the metric system, is inconsistent enough to use ½, ¼, ⅛, ¹⁄₁₆, ¹⁄₃₂, ¹⁄₆₄ of an inch and, in finer measurements, 0.001 of an inch. We English and Americans are stubborn, unmoved by the adoption of metric measurement in nearly all other countries.

Density of solids and liquids is expressed as the weight in grams of one cubic centimeter and since 1 cc. water at 4° C. weighs 1 gram, density is really relative to water. If one cubic centimeter of gold weighs 19.3 grams its density is 19.3. Did not Archimedes of ancient Syracuse determine the genuineness of the king's golden crown by weighing it after measuring its volume by the amount of water it displaced?

So accurate was Sir William Ramsay in determining the density of a gas that he weighed accurately a few cubic millimeters of radon, the mysterious gas coming off from radium. That was all he had of the precious element, yet his calculations of its molecular weight based upon that experiment were very reliable.

The floating spindle of glass, called a hydrometer, is a useful tool in determining the density of liquids. The concentration of sulfuric acid in a lead storage battery is commonly determined this way. When Chandler of Columbia introduced to milk dealers a special hydrometer or "lactometer" he showed them that a great part of New York City's milk supply of that day was watered. The simplicity of the test is a standing protection to the public.

The benefits to the dairy industry from the simple determination of the butter content of the milk, invented by Babcock of Wisconsin, are incalculable.

Temperature is measured by scientists in degrees Centigrade, the ideal method. The distance on the thermometer stem between the freezing point (0° C.) and the boiling point (100° C.) of water is 100° C. instead of 180° F. as on the common Fahrenheit scale. Heat itself is measured by the **calorie,** the amount of heat needed to raise the temperature of one gram of water one degree Centigrade. The heat evolved in some reaction taking place in a "calorimeter" may be calculated from the rise in temperature of a known weight of water surrounding the reaction chamber.

We even measure the inward pull on a drop of water or other liquid (surface tension), the concentration of sugar in cane juice by the angular rotation of polarized light, the slight alkalinity of the blood; but we are not prepared to make exact measurements of taste, although the best cooks compose symphonies for that sense, nor to measure odors, although the perfume master likewise blends his odor tones into great harmonies.

VI

THE LIGHTEST SUB-
STANCE KNOWN

THE DUTCH painter Teniers enriched the world with many pictures of medieval alchemists at work, but in none was self-delusion better depicted than in the scene where the weeping wife drops her last gold coin, not very hopefully, into the glowing crucible while her alchemist husband fans the fire into a ruddy glow. He, at least, is confident that the family gold will reappear, multiplied a hundredfold.

The painting does not show, however, an awkward elbow upsetting a bottle of acid on some chance scraps of iron. And if it had, the alchemist's eye, intent only on gold, might never have noticed a gas frothing up through the acid, a gas that would have burned had he thought to touch a glowing splinter to it. Thousands of times this accidental contact of acid and iron must have occurred in alchemistic dens yet none gave heed to the coming of a great power in human affairs. Opportunity knocked distinctly but ever so lightly at the door, for this unknown gas was hydrogen, the lightest substance in the world.

Not until Cavendish in England, about one hundred and seventy years ago, studied the properties of this gas was its identity as an element made certain, although Turquet de Mayerne a century earlier called it an "inflammable air." By the brilliant stroke of burning it in the oxygen newly discovered by Priestley and proving the product identical with water, Cavendish revealed the composition of water as an oxide of hydrogen. Nicholson and Carlisle closed the chapter by taking water apart—the parts were oxygen and hydrogen. Now you glibly call it H_2O although men drank more or less of it and bathed more or less often in it, and ships sailed the seas for thousands of years with little concern as to its real nature.

Water, then, is a limitless source of hydrogen and industry is already profiting thereby. But coal gas, a product of the coking of bituminous coal, is also utilized as a source in Europe where economic conditions permit. Every ton of this "soft" coal yields 27 pounds of free hydrogen which can be

Fig. 20. The last piece of the family gold is melted in the alchemist's crucible to coax a transformation of lead into precious metal.

separated from the other gases of distillation. By breaking down other compounds present, more could be obtained if desired.

When convenience rather than low cost is the main object, the combined hydrogen forming a part of all acids can be displaced by the more active and cheaper metals such as zinc or iron. Isn't it strange that hydrogen is found in sugar and the pure fiber of paper, yet gives them no sour or acidic taste, nor is it driven away from its moorings in the sugar molecule by any metal? Evidently the hydrogen atom in acid molecules is held to the other atoms in a different way.

Just to maintain a speaking acquaintance with equations you might, though you need not, glance at our brief story of the displacement of hydrogen from sulfuric acid or hydrochloric acid by zinc:

$$Zn + H_2SO_4 \rightarrow H_2 + ZnSO_4, \text{ zinc sulfate,}$$
$$Zn + 2HCl \rightarrow H_2 + ZnCl_2, \text{ zinc chloride.}$$

The hydrogen escapes while some sort of "salt" such as zinc sulfate, $ZnSO_4$, or zinc chloride, $ZnCl_2$, is left in the water solution.

If you arranged the metals in the order of the speed with which they drive out hydrogen from a given acid, the most active first, it would look like this:

Displacement Series of Metals

Potassium
Sodium
Barium
Strontium
Calcium
Magnesium
Aluminum
Manganese
Zinc
Cadmium
Iron
Nickel
Tin
Lead
Hydrogen
Copper
Mercury
Silver
Platinum
Gold

The metals below HYDROGEN in activity do not displace hydrogen at all. That explains the endurance of gold and platinum, for example. These metals are so indifferent to some acids and to many other chemicals that they were once called the "noble metals." On that basis copper which is just below hydrogen is merely patrician, certainly not royal like gold. Without doubt this chemical laziness accounts for their occurrence free in nature. The more active zinc, if it ever was free, hastened to unite with sulfur to form zinc sulfide, a well-known mineral, or with oxygen to produce another ore. So active are the top metals, sodium and potassium, that they displace hydrogen from cold water with flame and explosion. Iron, in the middle of the series, needs to have its courage bolstered up by red heat to displace hydrogen from steam.

Chemistry students learn something new every time they look at this Activity Series, or Displacement Series, or Electromotive Series of metals. As an illustration, take a pair of these metals, connect them with a wire and dip the metallic strips in a water solution of any acid, base (such as caustic soda, NaOH) or salt and you will have an electric battery with current flowing along the wire while the more active metal is eaten up. Furthermore the farther apart the two metals are in this useful series the greater the voltage of the battery or cell.

But to come back to our sources of hydrogen. There is plenty of it in the sun, if we could only get it. Flames of incandescent hydrogen 300,000 miles high and 100,000 miles wide burst out from the sun's chromosphere. But our own atmosphere contains only traces, thank Heaven! The college student who incautiously assured his professor that the air was a mixture of oxygen and hydrogen was urged never to light a match for if he escaped the violence of the explosive union of these two elements he would surely be drowned in the flood of water produced.

$$2H_2 + O_2 \rightarrow 2H_2O.$$

In the United States economic conditions are such that it pays well to make the enormous quantities of hydrogen now needed by passing steam over almost white-hot coke (carbon).

$$H_2O + C \rightarrow H_2 + CO, \text{ carbon monoxide.}$$

Naturally the coke is soon cooled by the steam below the reactive temperature, so every few minutes the valves are turned to shut off steam and to turn on a blast of air. The air burns some of the coke and heats up the rest quickly to 1000° C., ready for another blast of steam. Since the resulting gaseous mixture of hydrogen and carbon monoxide ($H_2 + CO$) is made from water (as well as from coke) it is called **water gas**. And since it is an excellent fuel it is made and sold in many cities.

The hydrogen can be separated for use. It can also be split off from hydrocarbons of the oil refinery by high-temperature "cracking."

Until about forty-three years ago hydrogen was chiefly known as the best lifting gas for balloons, as a good fuel for the blow-torch and as a helpful feature of the teaching discipline for chemistry classes. What would equations be without hydrogen? To be fair we must add that occasionally some professor of physics, after urging a boy with a bass voice to fill his lungs with hydrogen, suggests that the boy burst into song. The song is always tenor for vibration frequency of sound is greater in the lighter gases.

NOTE: All flames must be carefully extinguished to save the singer from bursting into something more than song.

The early balloon industry, although exciting enough, didn't call for much more hydrogen than the voice lessons described above. Then with the construction of enormous dirigibles, each swallowing millions of cubic feet of hydrogen, the case was somewhat different. Helium is safer.

In religion and in mythology man long ago dreamed of supermen with wings, so he must have an innate urge to soar into the blue empyrean.

It must, then, have seemed like a partial vindication of these hopes for the race when Joseph Montgolfier in France recklessly admitted two friends to the basket of the world's first passenger balloon, starting for parts unknown. This was in 1783 shortly after a trial trip with only a sheep and a rooster as crew—no pun intended there. When the alarmed animal and bird finally jumped out, their descent upon an unsuspecting French village aroused deep forebodings of disasters from Heaven.

The palmy days of balloon ascensions at county fairs and of international balloon races are not altogether ancient history. Now eminent scientists are lifted in strong aluminum spheres by balloons to a height of thirteen miles, more or less, in order that they may make important observations of the upper air. Captain Gray of the U. S. Army lost his life in 1927 by rising in a balloon to a height of a little over eight miles. A break in his oxygen breathing tube caused him to suffocate in the thin air of that great height. Observation balloons were used by armies in spying on the enemy forces until

FIG. 21. The first passenger balloon (1783).

airplanes served far better in World War II. Ship convoys in the English Channel were guarded by barrage balloons from which dangled steel wires.

But now hydrogen, refusing to continue in such minor rôles, steps to the very front and center of the world's stage. Kings may well give attention. Thanks to the genius of the German Haber, in 1913, hydrogen and the nitrogen of air were coaxed, even forced, to unite as ammonia, only a short and easy step removed from existence as one of the world's greatest fertilizers, ammonium sulfate, and only a quick and almost as easy step removed from existence as nitric acid, parent of high explosives, celluloid movie films, of some silks, and many other useful products.

FIG. 22. Only a few years ago American scientists, protected by a strong aluminum sphere and lifted by a giant balloon, explored the stratosphere, over thirteen miles above us.

Nor is this all. A Frenchman, Sabatier, delving in "pure science" discovered that, through the friendly aid of a trace of nickel (acting as a "catalyst"), hydrogen would add on to the molecules of various carbon compounds, a process called **hydrogenation.** Later it was found that liquid fats such as cottonseed oil could also add on hydrogen, perhaps 5000 cubic feet to the ton, if catalyzed by a trace of nickel. The liquid fat is said to be hardened for it can easily be given the consistency of lard for which it is now substituted as a cooking fat in convenient form.

Here they worked a good idea to the limit. Since you cannot make hard soaps out of liquid or unsaturated fats, why not harden the cottonseed oil, palm oil, soy bean oil, or the like with hydrogen and then cook the stuff with caustic soda to get a firm hard soap? Done, and very profitably, too. In this country alone 300,000,000 pounds of liquid fats are hydrogenated every year, equivalent, as far as lard production is concerned, to 7,000,000 hogs. Our greatest soap company gracefully acknowledged its indebtedness to the pure

SEVEN MILLION UNEMPLOYED HOGS RESENT HYDROGENATION

FIG. 23. With hydrogenation, our abundant liquid fats become solid enough for cooking convenience and for soap making.

research of Sabatier by handing him a generous and unexpected check at the same time that an American university bestowed upon the venerable Frenchman an honorary degree. He had previously received the Nobel prize.

Not content with hydrogenation of fats we have accomplished the forced addition of hydrogen under thousands of pounds pressure to coal, even to lignite. Germany has already, under the leadership of Bergius and others, produced great quantities of excellent liquid motor fuel by this method. The whip of necessity cracks over a great country practically barren of petroleum. With coal Germany can produce motor fuel although at the moment not in economic competition with petroleum. Government aid is required.

In our own country the Standard Oil Company of New Jersey led the way with some foreign patents in hydrogenating petroleum in order to create more gasoline than possible by other methods and to vary the nature of their products in accordance with changing market demands. The engineering difficulties have been surmounted and the process is in use. Apparently with proper high pressure, temperature and catalyst, we can hydrogenate all sorts of oils and tars to secure new and useful products.

Twenty-five years ago the Americans, Urey, Brickwedde and Murphy, discovered and isolated from water a remarkable form of hydrogen. It had been observed that the most accurate determinations of the atomic weight of hydrogen (relative to oxygen as the usual standard) by the best chemical methods and by the most delicate physical method ("positive ray analysis") failed to agree by a discrepancy of about one part in 5000. A clever observer suggested that if hydrogen contained an isotope of double the atomic weight of common hydrogen the physical method would come into perfect agreement with the chemical method. Isotopic forms of an element are alike chemically but different in the nucleus, therefore, in atomic weight. Urey assumed that if heavy hydrogen existed it might be concentrated to the point of detection, at least, by allowing a considerable quantity of liquid hydrogen to evaporate. Obviously the heavier molecules would evaporate more slowly than the lighter ones and so the last few drops of liquid should be much richer in double weight hydrogen. Brickwedde contributed 1 cc. of residual hydrogen remaining after evaporation of about 4 liters and this was examined by Urey and Murphy for the expected displacement of its spectral lines. Urey won on Thanksgiving Day, 1931. Double weight hydrogen was detected, but not isolated until later when Washburn showed that in the electrolysis of great quantities of water the last hydrogen to escape was much richer in the heavy isotope than is common hydrogen.

Never did hydrogen have such a place in the sun as now. Chemists are eagerly looking ahead to its greater future.

VII

THE ELIXIR OF LIFE

THIS IS a water world, like it or not. If any other liquid formed our oceans, made up over two thirds of the weight of our animal bodies and of plant tissues, formed our clouds and rain, affairs would soon be in a terrible tangle.

Of course we do very well, thank you, with "dry ice" (carbon dioxide snow), and we are trying out mercury vapor in place of the steam in power plants, and successfully using solid, crystalline ponds of photographers' "hypo" at Hollywood for hot-weather skating, but what if we traded all our present wealth of water for some such liquid as gasoline? At the touch of flame all the oxygen of the air would be consumed in burning some of the ocean. At last a premium would be put on stupidity, for the dullest oaf would probably be the man to "set the river on fire." Sugar sap would no longer rise in the sugar cane or the maple tree, for gasoline does not dissolve sugar. In fact, gasoline would fail dismally as a carrier for the contents of our present plant juices. Your own blood carries in solution certain salts, delicately balanced, not to mention other nourishments which are quite insoluble in gasoline.

No, we must admit that plain water is the real "elixir of life" so long sought by alchemists and by Ponce de León. Water has carried the burden of commerce for ages; made the earth's climate endurable by acting as a vapor blanket to regulate temperature; worn down flinty mountains and transported the resulting soil to the lowlands; and added, with its clouds, gratifying beauty to the outlook.

A single cubic mile of warm, moist summer air if suddenly chilled to freezing would flood the earth with 140,000 tons of water, but such cloudbursts are rare. One inch of rain in July on the corn belt of the United States is worth $400,-

000,000 to the farmer. On every acre this inch weighs 113 tons.

Light-hearted tenors sing rapturously of "The Land of the Sky Blue Water," but would they drink blue water, or reject it as coming from the laundry tub? Yet the poets and

Courtesy Machine Design

FIG. 24. Archimedes and his spiral water pump. Water has always been the vital liquid just as oxygen has always been the central element.

artists are right, water in very deep layers is blue. If you have a haunting and delightful memory of an emerald lake somewhere, consider the net color effect of blue water and a yellow sandy bottom, or of yellow suspended material. Optically such a combination spells green.

When those deep lakes freeze we ought to be grateful for the otherwise dry scientific fact that water is heaviest, densest, at exactly 4° C., a little above the freezing point, or in other words that ice floats. Most substances contract, get heavier, on cooling, but if ice sank our lakes would fill with solid ice from the bottom and never thaw out to any great depth. Fish would have a hard time of it, summer navigation would be limited to vessels of shallow draft and climate would be seriously affected.

While we are considering some of the fortunate properties of water we should have a warm feeling for its relatively high specific heat. Very few substances equal it in this respect. You remember from an earlier chapter that it requires one calorie of heat to raise one gram of water one degree Centigrade, and that, on cooling, this one calorie of heat is given off. The specific heat of water is exactly one, the standard, while that of most rocks is one fifth. Consequently land cools off rapidly as winter approaches while the oceans and lakes cool off far more slowly, thus moderating the climate. The reverse, though also moderating, effect is observed in early spring.

What would Great Britain do without the tremendous number of calories of heat carried from the warm Gulf of Mexico by the Gulf Stream? Similarly the Japanese current warms our own Oregon and Washington. If water had no higher specific heat than dry land the climate of Britain would be but little milder than that of Labrador. To be more personal, if it were not for this very high specific heat of the water making up most of the weight of your body, vigorous exercise would raise your temperature to a dangerous, perhaps fatal, extent.

Engineers sometimes speculate on the possibility of building a great deflecting barrier off Newfoundland to divert the chilly Arctic current away from New England. Old England would have something to say about that.

French engineers once dreamed of cutting a sea level canal from the Atlantic in order to flood a low section of the Sahara Desert. The enormous lake thus formed would probably bring rains to Europe as well as to North Africa and so might have international consequences.

The general public may not think of water as a "chemical" but it is, and the one most used in the laboratory. If water did not react with chlorine the latter probably could not bleach cotton cloth nor kill bacteria as effectively as it does. Even ammonia gas reacts with water to form the useful "aqua ammonia," a base. And so does quicklime, or there would be no common mortar and plaster [$CaO + H_2O \rightarrow Ca(OH)_2$], or plaster of Paris, $CaSO_4 + 2H_2O \rightarrow CaSO_4 \cdot 2H_2O$. There would be fewer museum reproductions of classic Greek statues and details of great architecture.

Differences in properties of deuterium oxide or "heavy water" and hydrogen oxide or common water (D_2O and H_2O) are those of degree rather than of kind. Yet these differences are interesting.

	Heavy water	Common water
Density	1.1007	1.000
Boiling point	101.4° C.	100° C.
Freezing point	+ 3.8° C.	0° C.

The price of 99.5 per cent pure heavy water has now fallen from the earlier figures of $150 and $5 per gram to much much less in the U. S. and Norway. More research, chemical, biological and physical, with this remarkable material becomes feasible. The source, at present, is the residual liquid left after electrolysis of enormous quantities of common water. The final fraction in the evaporation of liquefied hydrogen is another source.

Without the reaction of water with Portland cement

powder to form a solid rock, there would be no concrete roads, or buildings, or dams, or tunnels, or sidewalks. A muddy road is not surfaced with a compound of dust and water but with a mere mechanical mixture of the two. How different is the product obtained by adding water to the dust known as Portland cement. A chemical reaction takes place, yielding a new compound, hard as a rock. If there were no reaction the wet stuff would form just another mud road.

Sometimes industry is extremely anxious to get rid of

FIG. 25. When Witigis, king of the Goths, brought his hordes to the siege of Rome in the year 537, he dealt a deadly blow at the city by striking at the aqueducts which furnished Rome with water.

water, in other words to dry things, from green lumber to fruits and vegetables. Flash-dried egg powder has become good army food. Milk sprayed through fine nozzles or atomizers into a current of hot, dry air is quickly, in a fraction of a minute, converted into dry powder which keeps well and is an excellent food. The development of bad tastes by oxidation in the air is prevented through sheer lack of time. Even some salts are "spray dried" from solution in order to secure tiny spherulites or pellets which are convenient in handling and which take up less moisture from the air during storage.

If anyone insists that transportation lines are the arteries of a great city we must stipulate that the great aorta is the water main. Even mighty Rome weakened and fell into the hands of barbarians when her aqueducts were cut.

New York City leads an underground river from the Catskill Mountains, 150 miles away, to a distributing system 600 feet below the pavements. Over 5,000 miles of cast-iron mains carry this life-giving flood to consumers. Several hundred million gallons daily are demanded by this voracious city. If urban dwellers now had to pay one cent a gallon as they generally did in 1800 for water peddled in barrels, the daily bill for New Yorkers would total $10,000,000. As it is, many cities are able to retail water at the meter at the rate of 100 gallons for one cent. Manufacturers of cast-iron pipe claim the credit, and certainly much of it is theirs, although the big conduits may be rock tunnels lined with smooth concrete.

The average city of 100,000 uses 10,000,000 gallons daily, only half a gallon per capita as a beverage or in cooking, and 30 gallons for other household uses such as cleaning, bathing, etc. The rest is needed by industry, the fire department, and street cleaning. But the quality of the 50,000 gallons used for drinking must be maintained by the entire 10,000,000 gallons.

"Safety first," is the slogan of every water department and in this country municipal water supplies are almost universally free from dangerous bacteria. This freedom is secured by care of the drainage basins to prevent sewage contamination at the source, by filtering, and by treatment with chlorine. Only two and a half pounds per million gallons is needed so the cost is negligible, but the public maintains that the taste is far from negligible. This taste is enormously aggravated when wastes from by-product coke ovens are allowed to contaminate the water, for chlorine and phenols react to form most offensive compounds. This, however, is preventable as well as unusual.

A successful development that is well worth general adoption is the treatment of the water with extremely small quantities of very porous carbon, stirred in as a fine powder and removed by a filter. Remarkable results in removal of taste are now being obtained.

In 1880 deaths from typhoid fever in twelve states reached the alarming total of 55 per 100,000 population. By 1927 the typhoid death rate for 32,000,000 city population had dwindled to 1.96 per 100,000. The gain was not all due to chlorination of water supplies, however, for improvement in the milk supply was a tremendous factor.

A DOLLAR PER 100 GALLONS

Cast Iron Pipe Association

FIG. 26. Water was expensive in New York and Philadelphia during Colonial times. Today one hundred gallons may be had for one cent.

The quality of town water in Europe centuries ago, or even much later, was notoriously bad, causing great spread of disease. On this ground some historians suggest that perhaps those who drank wine, beer, tea or coffee instead of bacteria-infested water lived longer and better, that the population really could not have survived on a water diet. It is easy to see where this argument leads us, so it will be wiser to steer for safer waters.

The growth of Los Angeles will probably be limited by its water supply, now brought a great distance from the Colorado River. Even now a shortage is in sight so the city considers how it may use its water twice. As an experiment and with no desire to frighten residents away "the Los Angeles sanitary engineers are now daily converting

200,000 gallons of the city's dirtiest sewage into pure, clear, sparkling water which analysis shows to be equal in quality to the regular city water. Although the source of this water cannot possibly be detected by odor or taste, it is not being returned to the city mains on account of sales resistance on the part of the public." Perhaps a second system of pipe lines will supply this water for rougher uses.

Esselen calls this "laundering the sewage" and points out that all the cities along the Ohio River practically do this very thing, with no objection from the public, because Nature helps purify the river. Sewage purification at Los Angeles is secured by "activated sludge," a growth of bacteria and enzymes, which converts the watery mixture into an inoffensive black solid used as fertilizer, a fuel gas, and clear water. A further treatment with activated sludge is followed by aeration, chlorination, settling, charcoal dosing, and filtration. The superintendent then drinks the perfect product. We may here answer any foolish questions about the possible use of sea water at Los Angeles by reminding you that salt water is not popular as a beverage, that it kills grass, and corrodes boilers. No softener can remove this salt for practically all sodium compounds are soluble. There can be no argument about the wisdom of compelling all cities so to dispose of sewage instead of overloading our streams with untreated material. The scientists have done their part—will politicians and tax payers do theirs?

The remaining quality in water demanded by the public is freedom from excessive hardness. In the limestone areas especially, water dissolves salts of calcium and magnesium. On heating in a boiler, the bicarbonates are converted into insoluble carbonates and upon complete evaporation the sulfates and chlorides are also deposited as the costly boiler scale. Costly is the right word, for a compact layer of these salts one-eighth inch thick on the boiler wall causes a fuel loss of ten per cent. Hot water heating pipes gradually become clogged when very hard water is used. Then to make bad matters worse these calcium and magnesium salts react with soap (wasting the soap) to form sticky, greasy, curds of calcium soaps which nobody wants.

Problem: how to soften hard water. Industrial plants do it by precipitating the calcium and magnesium with lime and soda, but not many cities as yet see fit to do this for all.

The village of Oberlin, Ohio, was the first municipality in the United States to soften the public water supply, while Columbus is the largest city to adopt the process. It can be done profitably on a large scale.

There are even those who believe that cities can afford to soften water by the use of artificial zeolites more effectively, though more expensively. Hotels, some factories, and private homes now do this. Hardness is removed by mere filtration through a layer of the material which is occasionally regenerated by soaking in salt water. The process is really quite simple and softens beyond the power of any added chemicals.

To the importance of water to steam power, transportation, agriculture, weather, beauty, and health we may add its value as a dirt remover, in gold mining, washing away a Seattle hill, in making concrete roads, meshing cellulose fibers together to form paper, and as a great commercial source of hydrogen.

At Hoover Dam massive cylindrical gates in towers 358 feet high "now subdue a torrential Colorado River and unleash captive floods to irrigate a vast arid waste and to supply millions of horse power for populous communities."

VIII

WHEN WILL IT FREEZE?

EVERYONE KNOWS that water freezes at 32° Fahrenheit or, as scientists say, zero Centigrade, and that salt water must be cooled below this point before it turns to ice. Suppose you wanted to calculate how much salt you must dissolve in a quart of water to keep it from freezing at — 5° Centigrade. How would you do it?

However you are more interested in knowing how much glycerine or alcohol or glycol to put in the water of your auto radiator in order to prevent "freezing up" of the car in cold weather.

Perhaps a consideration of solutions applies. You remember from an earlier chapter that in a gas individual molecules fly around like a swarm of bees with nothing but space between them—a sort of molecular dispersion in nothing. Now imagine that you have filled in those spaces with water or other liquid. The molecules will not fly around as freely as before and you will have a molecular dispersion in a liquid—a solution. As a matter of fact we make solutions in simpler ways, as by dropping a lump of sugar into a cup of tea. Here the water slips in between the ultimate particles of sugar, the molecules, and separates them into a homogeneous mixture of water and sugar, a solution. We hasten to remind you that water has a sweet tooth, for not all liquids can dissolve this sugar, certainly not gasoline. Honors are even when it comes to any attempt to dissolve a fat—there the solvent rôles of water and gasoline are reversed.

You have, perhaps, noticed that very fine powders stirred up with water are slow to settle, the finer the slower, but that they do settle. Not so with true solutions. They never settle, if placed in a well-corked bottle to prevent evaporation.

It was a keen observer who first noticed that 1000 cubic

centimeters (one liter) of water in which 32 grams of wood alcohol, CH_3OH, was dissolved, froze at $-1.86°$ Centigrade, and that one liter of water in which was dissolved 92 grams of glycerine, also froze at $-1.86°$ Centigrade. The exciting point here is the fact that 32 grams of wood alcohol and 92 grams of glycerine contain exactly the same number of molecules, in fact the relative weights of their molecules are 32 and 92. It is convenient to speak of the 32 grams as the "gram molecular weight" of wood alcohol, CH_3OH. Count up the weights of all the atoms in CH_3OH and you get the molecular weight.

But this isn't all of it. Experimenters tried dissolving exactly the known gram molecular weights of many soluble substances in one liter of water and in every case (except with acids, bases, salts) no ice would form until the various solutions were cooled 1.86 degrees below zero, Centigrade. By this time your scientific reasoning compels you to generalize, a safe procedure only after many observations. You tell the world that molecules are very democratic, that a light molecule counts just as much as a heavy one in lowering the freezing point of water. Taste, color, odor, size, politics, are reckoned as nothing, it is only *number of dissolved particles,* or molecules, that brings down the freezing point. Evidently it is not just pounds of "antifreeze" that you want to put in the water of your car radiator, it is number of soluble molecules.

Now granting that you believe that exactly one molecular weight, counted as grams, of many different substances lowers the freezing point of one liter of water exactly $1.86°$ C., how could you determine the molecular weight of a brand-new substance that you extracted from the seeds of a tree on one of your exploring expeditions up the Amazon? Isn't it simple, now that you have reasoned it out? Yes, you could keep on dissolving your precious powder in one liter of water and trying to freeze it by suitable refrigeration until you just hit a concentration that froze precisely at $-1.86°$ C. Suppose it took 85 grams of your new substance to accomplish this.

Naturally there must be just as many molecules in the 85 grams as in the 32 grams of wood alcohol mentioned above or in a gram molecular weight of any other substance equally effective in lowering the freezing point of water. Therefore 85 is the molecular weight of your Amazon discovery. In actual practise you would make up any convenient concentration and freeze it. By considering proportionate weights and proportionate lowerings it would be easy to calculate how many grams you should have taken to get the − 1.86° C. freezing point.

NON-FREEZE MIXTURES FOR CAR RADIATORS
Percentage by Volume, in Water

Freezing Temperature, F.	Denatured Alcohol	Wood Alcohol	Distilled Glycerine	Ethylene Glycol
20°	19	12	22	16
10°	30	20	32	25
0°	38	29	40	32
−10°	45	34	47	39
−20°	52	40	54	44

Now examine the preceding table of non-freeze mixtures for your car. Although it is a "practical" table and does not list molecular weights nor even common weights its volume concentration indicates roughly that an added quart, or liter, of liquids with smaller molecules, like wood alcohol, is more effective than an equal volume of glycerine with fewer, because much larger, molecules. There are more molecules in a quart of wood alcohol than in a quart of glycerine, and it is only number of molecules that counts.

Explosions from rapid thawing of frozen dynamite are now rare because the manufacturer adds dinitrotoluene or other substances to lower the freezing point of the nitroglycerine present.

When the sap in wheat freezes the tissues of the plant are damaged. A laboratory test of the freezing point of expressed sap may indicate which wheat can better stand extreme winters. The sap of evergreen leaves must have enough dissolved material to lower the freezing point safely. As a matter of fact summer sap in the same evergreen is so "thin" that it would actually freeze with damage to the tree if it were subjected to low winter temperatures. Nature steps in and sees to it by late fall that insoluble starches in the leaves are changed into soluble sugars and the like, making the sap very difficult to freeze.

Have you forgotten that a page or so back we excepted "acids, bases, and salts" from our sweeping statements? Here is the reason. If we tell you that the molecular weight of common salt is 58 you would have every reason to expect that 58 grams of it dissolved in one liter of water would lower the freezing point 1.86° below the usual freezing point of water, zero Centigrade. Actually the solution freezes at nearly twice 1.86° Centigrade below zero. Now be firm and stand by your original conclusion soundly based upon many experiments, that equal numbers of particles produce equal lowerings of the freezing point. Then why this abnormally large value for salt, almost twice that expected by experiment with sugar, glycerine, alcohol, and many others?

There is only one answer—each molecule of salt, NaCl, split into two particles, or at least most of them did. The salt molecule is made up of just two atoms so they must separate.

$$NaCl \rightarrow Na + Cl.$$

Unthinkable, for we know that common metallic sodium, represented by the symbol Na, reacts violently with water, nor have we forgotten that chlorine gas, Cl_2, is greenish yellow, irritating, and poisonous. In a glass of salt water there is no color, no explosion, no "death in the cup." But logic is logic. More particles, greater lowering of the freezing point. Unexpectedly great lowering, unexpected increase in number of particles, possible only by division of those already present.

"Well," we insist, "those sodium particles simply cannot be common, everyday sodium, nor are the chlorine particles common chlorine."

Try passing a direct current of electricity through a glass of salt water and you will find the secret of it all. Greenish yellow chlorine escapes at one electrode, the positive pole, while the sodium travels over to the negative electrode and would appear as a layer on that pole if it were not for the presence of the water. Sodium metal and water always fight, with hydrogen gas and caustic soda, NaOH, as the result of their quarrel. Isn't it strange that those are the very products (secondary ones) at the negative pole, the cathode? The only reason all the colorless chlorine particles should travel to the positive electrode must be an attraction due to an opposite charge of electricity (negative) on these chlorine atoms. Yes, they are different, they are chlorine ions, Cl^-, and by similar logic the sodium atoms must be attracted to the negative electrode because they are sodium ions, Na^+, positively charged. Opposites attract. Of course the sodium ions give up their charge to the negative electrode and then react with the water present. Similarly the chlorine ions are discharged at the positive pole.

$$NaCl \rightarrow Na^+ + Cl^-.$$

How well all this fits in with the fact that only acids, bases, and salts in water solution conduct a current of electricity. It is these charged atoms, or even groups of atoms, that carry the current, ferry it across the river. Sugar in water carries no current. All acids in water yield charged hydrogen atoms or ions, H^+, and it is these ions that give the sour taste, attack many metals and carbonates, and ruin bases.

$$HCl \rightarrow H^+ + Cl^-.$$

All bases, caustic soda for example, yield hydroxide ions, OH^-, in water.

$$NaOH \rightarrow Na^+ + OH^-.$$

An acid and a base ruin each other's characteristic properties because the hydrogen ions discharge the hydroxyl ions with formation of water. Don't bother with the rest of it.

$$H^+ + OH^- \rightarrow H_2O.$$

So now you understand **ionization**, and **electrolysis**, and even the **neutralization** of an acid by a base. What is silver plating to you now except the attraction of silver ions, Ag^+, in a solution of a silver salt, to a negatively charged metal spoon or knife, followed by electric discharge against the spoon and deposition of a layer of ordinary silver?

If you need an extra argument with which to convince skeptics remember that HCl gas in water solution, your old friend hydrochloric acid, attacks zinc and marble (a carbonate) while this same HCl gas dissolved in toluene does none of these things. In water the HCl molecules break apart into ions, $H^+ + Cl^-$, but in toluene there are only dissolved molecules, no ions.

It is worth adding that melted salts ionize, conduct electricity, and are decomposed in so doing. Otherwise there would be only limited quantities of very expensive aluminum on the market, and no magnesium at all.

The most recent theory warns us that solid acids, bases and salts are made up of these charged particles or ions arranged in a geometric pattern, each ion adjoining ions of opposite charge. Water merely pries these units apart and melting the solid dry merely gives great freedom of motion. This "space lattice" of certain crystalline material was revealed by X-ray photographs.

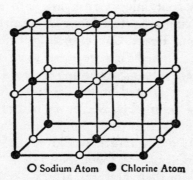

O Sodium Atom ● Chlorine Atom

Cubic arrangement of atoms in a
crystal of sodium chloride.

IX

CHEMICAL WARFARE

WHEN THE German army at Ypres, during the afternoon of April 22, 1915, let loose on the breeze greenish-yellow clouds of poisonous chlorine gas and broke the Allied line, they marked the beginning of a new era in modern warfare.

But this was not really the first time that noxious fumes or smokes were used to demoralize an enemy. The Athenians and Spartans as early as 431 B.C. burned sulfur and pitch against the walls of enemy cities. "Greek fire," a mixture of lime, pitch, sulfur, resin and petroleum, was used by the Emperor Constantine against the Saracens about 673 A.D. and, centuries later, used by Saracens against Christians during the Crusades. Col. W. Lee Lewis, inventor of Lewisite, insists that the earliest effective use of demoralizing fumes or sprays in warfare was by the *mephitus Americanus,* commonly known and feared as the skunk.

The British considered the use of burning sulfur at the siege of Sebastopol in the Crimean War but rejected the plan as inhumane, although probably effective. During the siege of Charleston in 1863 the Federal general, Gilmore, threw a number of shells containing Greek fire into the city but desisted after receiving a protest from General Beauregard.

At The Hague Peace Conference in 1899 the strongest nations of Europe signed an agreement to refrain from using projectiles charged with asphyxiating gases. Germany signed a little later, but the United States delegate, Admiral Mahan, was instructed by John Hay, Secretary of State, to refuse to sign on the grounds that such an agreement could not be enforced and that gas warfare would probably be no worse than the use of firearms and torpedoes.

The Germans in their first gas attack "kept the letter but not the spirit" of their pledge. Later they used shells and bombs as more effective in placing gas exactly where needed. The great rolling clouds of chlorine released from thousands of cylinders were carried by a favoring breeze to the line of French colonials and Canadians. Unprepared as the Allied soldiers were for such a mysterious attack, they broke, after several thousand lives were lost in hopeless defense. The way was open to the coveted Channel ports—but the Germans were overcautious, not realizing how effective their attack had been. Then they had no gas masks for their own protection. Soon the Canadians re-formed the line and almost overnight cloths and sponges were saturated with soda and with photographer's "hypo" to be used as the first gas masks. Both of these harmless chemicals react with chlorine to form such harmless substances as sodium chloride (common table salt).

However the next great gas attack, in the following December, was not with chlorine but with phosgene mixed with chlorine. Fortunately for the Allies their spies secured detailed information about the phosgene well in advance and, as a result, the proper gas masks were ready. From then on it was a race between gas and gas mask, with a constant threat from several deadly chemicals.

Chlorine was essential to the manufacture of practically all the effective war gases so its production was greatly stimulated. By the end of the war one plant at Edgewood Arsenal, near Baltimore, was producing 50-100 tons of chlorine daily.

Little did Scheele, the Swedish drug clerk, dream when he first released the element chlorine from hydrochloric acid in 1774, that he was unleashing the dogs of war. Scheele really oxidized hydrochloric acid, not directly with oxygen of air, but with different substances capable of giving up oxygen. The effect, in principle, was

$$O_2 + 4HCl \rightarrow 2H_2O + 2Cl_2, \text{ chlorine.}$$

Never mind the details but you might well ask where Scheele first caught the rabbit for his rabbit pie, in other words how he made the HCl, hydrochloric acid. That was known long before. Mere heating of common salt with concentrated sulfuric acid caused an evolution of a colorless gas, technically called hydrogen chloride but in water solution, hydrochloric acid. Sodium sulfate, Na_2SO_4, is the by-product.

$$2NaCl + H_2SO_4 \rightarrow 2HCl + Na_2SO_4.$$

The modern method of manufacture of chlorine is electrolysis of salt water. Chlorine gas escapes at one electrode and valuable sodium hydroxide (caustic soda, $NaOH$) is formed at the other. Which of the two is to be called the by-product depends upon relative demand and prices. Each helps lower the cost of the other.

There is no lack of raw material for the manufacture of chlorine, for the United States alone produces 15,000,000 tons of salt yearly. Great salt beds are common, even found below our cities, notably Detroit and Cleveland. The latter actually produces 75,000 tons of salt annually within the city limits, pumped up as salt brine, later to be evaporated.

There is little need to discourse upon the animal craving for salt, its importance in food preservation, nor even to remind you that salt was once used as money, that the oppressive tax on salt by French kings led to revolution and that Gandhi made salt an issue against the British rule in India. But perhaps you have never considered what complicated industries could be founded upon a bed of salt. In Syracuse, New York, it is soda, not made by the original Le Blanc process but by the more modern Solvay process, using as raw materials salt, limestone, and ammonia. At Midland, Michigan, it is chlorine, sodium hydroxide, and a long list of chemicals such as carbolic acid (phenol), indigo, aspirin, metallic magnesium, bromine, calcium chloride, that can be made indirectly from salt or its natural impurities.

Of soda this country uses 5,000,000 tons yearly, and of sodium hydroxide (caustic soda) over 3,500,000 tons.

No wonder chlorine was effective as a war gas. It attacks some metals, recovers the thin tin coating on scrap tin sheet in the form of useful tin chloride, and reacts with the thinnest copper foil or leaf so fast that flame is sometimes produced. Think of copper burning in an atmosphere of chlorine! And what an easy equation this suggests.

$$Cu + Cl_2 \rightarrow CuCl_2, \text{ copper chloride.}$$

We can go further with this broad conception of combustion. Burn a jet of natural gas (mostly methane, CH_4) in a bottle of chlorine gas and you see a flame accompanied by a dense cloud of black smoke, carbon, of course. A simple test also shows the presence of much hydrochloric acid, HCl. A glance at the equation explains everything. Evidently chlorine is so active that it can steal the hydrogen out of methane and many other hydrogen compounds.

$$CH_4 + 2Cl_2 \rightarrow 4HCl + C, \text{ carbon.}$$

And now to show how simple it is to use chlorine in the production of still more effective war gases, such as the deadly lewisite, phosgene, chlorpicrin, and mustard gas. Mere passing of a mixture of chlorine with carbon monoxide over an active (ultraporous) charcoal at a moderately elevated temperature yields phosgene, $COCl_2$

$$CO + Cl_2 \rightarrow COCl_2.$$

The carbon merely acts as a catalyst, lends friendly help to the reaction. Phosgene is a gas, except in very cold weather, and so is quickly blown away by breezes. In World War I this gas was used only in explosive shells, to save waste and to carry it farther. It was easily stopped by gas masks containing a layer of quicklime and caustic soda. What a terrible wolf in sheep's clothing, or rather in corn husks, this phosgene is. At the first faint whiff the soldier imagines he is smelling fresh sweet corn, then the acid, corrosive attack on lungs sets in.

Then came the curious development of tear gases—either chloracetophenone or brombenzyl cyanide—not particularly toxic but useful in compelling the enemy to don gas masks with consequent loss of physical activity. A soldier must work to draw air through the mask. Still stranger was the use of sneezing gases, really smokes of solid particles scattered by shell explosions, which went right through the mask chemicals and forced the victim to sneeze his mask off, thus making him vulnerable to toxic gases. The agonized prayers that went out for a defensive against this and other more toxic smokes were finally answered by the simplest thing in the world—a layer of felt, from the soldier's felt hat, if you prefer. Somehow the tortuous channels of a wad of felt in the mask stopped the deadly smokes, and saved thousands of lives.

The next trick was the use of liquid chlorpicrin, CCl_3NO_2, easily prepared from chlorine, lime, and picric acid. Sprays

FIG. 27. Without gas masks an army today would be at the mercy of a modern enemy.

from exploding shells forced the soldier to tear off his mask because of excessive vomiting. Drops on the ground or clothing persisted longer than gases and forced extra precautions. Improved masks finally met this menace.

The triumph, if such it may be called, of the gas-makers' art was mustard gas, dichlorodiethylsulfide, or $S(C_2H_4Cl)_2$. It is a heavy, oily liquid, unfortunately nearly odorless, giving off its distinctive vapors from drops scattered on ground, clothing, trees, etc., for a few days. Its terrible effectiveness is due to its penetration of the skin and later its slow reaction with water in the cells of the body to form hydrochloric acid. Its use is really a trick to get hydrochloric acid in deep beneath the protective skin. Gas masks keep it out of the lungs but special protective uniforms must be worn to keep it out of the body. Protective salves have been developed.

Mustard gas was king of them all and probably will never be excelled, except by the more recent paralyzing nerve gas which is now held in reserve, a terrible threat. The raw materials are sulfur, chlorine, and ethylene, C_2H_4, the last named a by-product of petroleum refining, or obtainable by the dehydration of alcohol. Note the terrible simplicity of the reactions.

$$S_2 + Cl_2 \rightarrow S_2Cl_2, \text{ sulfur chloride,}$$
$$S_2Cl_2 + 2C_2H_4 \rightarrow S + S(C_2H_4Cl)_2, \text{ mustard gas.}$$

During a ten-day attack, over a million shells filled with mustard gas were thrown.

Lewisite, very similar in action, was made in Cleveland from acetylene and arsenic trichloride, but never actually used. It is less persistent in moist air and is very dangerous in manufacture.

At the end of that war Germany and England were each producing 30 tons daily of war gases but the United States at Edgewood Arsenal was making 200 tons daily. It was fear of the tremendous attack planned by the Allies with this superiority in gas that caused the sudden German capitulation. A magnificent gas threat saved thousands of lives.

After World War I some statistics were prepared by the Surgeon-General of the United States, statistics so astounding as to create doubts of their reliability in the minds of prejudiced haters of chemical warfare. But Great Britain and other nations soon corroborated these figures with similar records of their own.

Weapons, other than gas, caused 6,264,507 casualties in the American, British, and German armies, and of these "hospital cases" 2,552,931 or 40.7 per cent died. There were 330,396 casualties from gas and of these only 9763 or 2.9 per cent died. In other words a soldier so badly disabled that first aid treatment could not patch him up had about fourteen times as good a chance for life if he had been gassed as if he had been mangled by bayonet, bullet, or shrapnel. "But," argued the critics, "the poor fellow's lungs were so scarred that he later became a victim of tuberculosis." Again the cold, inexorable facts disprove wild assertions. Our Surgeon-General studied 3000 gas victims through the years following the war and compared them with 3000 other soldiers. If anything, there were actually fewer cases of pulmonary disease among gassed soldiers than among the others.

Will you be guilty of a sweeping generalization based upon one or two terrible instances of gas effects that you have seen or will you be scientific and compare a large number of instances?

By this time our gentle reader has acquired the scientific attitude towards facts and can face them without the blind, unreasoning prejudice of the common mob. He will probably admit now that chemical warfare is considerably less horrible than other kinds. Col. W. Lee Lewis describes the ideal war as confined to the use of harmless anesthetics and handcuffs. The French, perhaps, noisily explode bombs over the German lines, spraying these anesthetics on the enemy and then after a polite interval rush over and tie up or handcuff the insensible Germans. A glorious and bloodless victory without the loss of a man, and the war is ended!

Question—which type of present-day warfare comes nearest the humorous ideal outlined by the kind-hearted colonel? It must be the type that sends armies to the hospital for a few weeks or months with a 97 or 98 per cent hope of recovery—this much misunderstood and maligned chemical warfare.

The public is always against it because it sounds "hellish" and one of our greatest generals voted against it—after he passed the age of 60. How interesting, on the other hand, that a test vote among American Legion veterans showed their preference for gas warfare to other types, at least they did not want it abolished first. Perhaps the older strategists trained to use of rifle, bayonet, and cannon instinctively look upon any radically different weapon as contrary to the rules of the game. So it was with that perfect flower of chivalry, Sir Knight Bayard, who promptly put to death captives caught toting the new fire-belching blunderbuss, yet treated gently and kindly "captive wielders of brain-spattering battle ax or flesh-carving sword." The ancient Romans felt that the short sword was the only glorious weapon yet with this "humane" weapon Hannibal's army killed 48,000 Romans in one day.

Can we successfully ban chemical warfare by international agreement? Probably not, for two reasons. When a nation, fighting in a just cause (as they all believe) has its back to the wall, facing a terrible future, it will resort to any effective weapon—if history really repeats itself. Second, a deceitful, treacherous nation, or government, rather, can sign an agreement while secretly manufacturing war gases. It is too easy to avoid detection. Oh, a brilliant idea dawns! Let us ban the manufacture of the chlorine so necessary to the manufacture of nearly all the toxic gases. Yes, and thereby stop the chlorination of city water supplies and doom thousands to death by typhoid fever, stop the bleaching of cotton cloth and interfere with several useful manufactures. For that matter an individual could hide and operate an electrolytic chlorine cell in his own cellar as safely, almost, as he could operate an illicit still.

Our greatest fear, however, is for civilians in ruthless war. Before the atomic bomb threat Europe studied the best civilian defense against gas attack. So did the United States. Japan drilled its urban population in gas defense and England considered the manufacture of gas masks for every civilian. But the civilian case, although serious enough, is not nearly so bad as sensational writers make out—or make up. On approach of bombing planes the city population should retreat to the upper floors, close all windows and doors, shut off ventilating devices—and wait for breezes to blow away the toxic gases, smokes and mists. With gases proper this means a very short wait, but mustard droplets persist, volatilizing slowly. However, a masked fire department could profitably hose down the streets and perhaps the roof areas (really the greater fraction of a city area) or the city could be gassed by its own citizens with chemicals which clean up mustard by converting it into harmless compounds. Bleaching powder is effective.

Military strategists even now announce that gas planes will also drop explosive bombs powerful enough to shatter windows, thus allowing the toxic vapors to enter.

Here is a golden opportunity for the non-shatterable glass used in some automobiles or, cheaper yet, for some sort of strong translucent fabric that could quickly be set in the window like a common wire screen. In war time all the people in especially vulnerable cities might be equipped with masks. Unfortunately no mask can protect against atomic bomb destruction.

It may comfort the uneasy New Yorker to learn that although 20 milligrams of mustard gas placed exactly in the lungs may be fatal it actually took two tons during the war to secure a single death or twenty-nine casualties. Careful calculation indicates that 14,000 airplanes carrying a ton each of phosgene would be required to gas New York effectively.

Since gas is particularly powerful as a defensive weapon Mills suggests the following text for treaties regulating such warfare. "The signatory powers bind themselves not to use beyond the limits of their own territory, gases or other chemical agents capable of producing fatalities in the concentration used."

"It's an ill wind that blows nobody good"; and that is absolutely true of chemical warfare. The desperate necessity of inventing an adequate gas mask forced chemical research to a fierce intensity, for the fate of empires hung in the balance while the chemists strove desperately in the laboratory. Out of it came an ultra-porous charcoal that strained out of the air most toxic gases. Now the sword has been truly beaten into pruning hooks for this adsorbent charcoal today recaptures, condenses, from factory air 200,000 tons of the volatile solvents of industry, worth in an ordinary year $50,000,000.

The mask itself is donned by workmen condemned to repair broken ammonia pipes in refrigeration plants. And it should have been at hand for rescuers in the Cleveland Clinic X-ray film fire of years ago when carbon monoxide, hydrocyanic acid, and red-brown nitrogen dioxide gases killed 124 persons.

Taking a leaf out of the books of war, airplanes now dust cotton fields with calcium arsenate dust in an attack on the cotton boll weevil and then turn to pine forests endangered by a tree borer. Dusting from the air is the only defense against the annual loss of $90,000,000 to the pine forests of Oregon and Northern California. Ethyl mercaptan with its disgusting odor may be mixed with city gas in order to show up leaks. Marine borers, so destructive to harbor piling, are attacked by soaking the timbers in war gas derivatives. Ships are fumigated with hydrocyanic acid gas mixed with the very odorous cyanogen chloride to give warning. Ship barnacles are kept off by toxic paints developed by our Chemical Warfare Service.

Most important of all, however, is the merciful use of tear gas bombs in dispersing mobs. No longer is it inevitable that two or three policemen be shot when some maniac or desperate criminal barricades himself in a house and defies arrest. A few tear gas bombs hurled through the windows generally bring out the desperado.

Chlorine has three interesting and useful relatives, bromine, iodine, and fluorine, which form very similar compounds, for example: HCl, HBr, HI, and HF, their simpler acids.

The gaseous element fluorine is of no commercial interest partly because it is the fiercest tiger in the chemical menagerie, the most active element known. But its salts, the fluorides, are necessary to the manufacture of aluminum, and its simple organic compound, Freon, is the safe cooling gas in your household refrigerator.

Iodine, the violet black solid, made from seaweed ash, brines, and an impurity in Chile saltpeter, is of personal interest to us all because any abnormality in the iodothyroxin content of our thyroid glands spells goiter of one type or another. The human body ought to contain about 25 milligrams of combined iodine, all of it obtained, of course, from our drinking water and from food, especially vegetables. Since the natural sodium iodide in many soils has been leached out by streams there are "goiter belts" in this country and in Switzerland, too. Feeding school children exactly the right, and very minute, quantity of sodium iodide greatly decreased the percentage of goiter in Switzerland. In the United States iodized table salt is sold in most groceries and is quite safe to use. Salt spray from the ocean blows far inland and furnishes plenty of iodides to water and plants. South Carolina is now advertising with pardonable vanity the unusually high iodide content of her string beans and other vegetables.

Although iodine was inexpensively produced in Chile as a by-product of their nitrate production, their virtual monopoly permitted Chilean producers to hold up the price (and our people) at $4.00 per pound. After some enterprising Americans extracted iodine from the salt brine of a California oil well our consumers were given the benefit of a generous price cut to less than half the former cost. Chile cut below our own cost of production, finally to $0.90 per pound in 1936. If tariff protection was ever needed in order to stimulate and reward American enterprise this was a clear case.

Bromine, a volatile red-black liquid, made in this country from impurities in salt beds, may recall to you a famous sedative but it should make you think of the whole art of photography with movie and talkie included, for without light-sensitive silver bromide, photography, though not impossible, would be in a bad way.

Closer yet, perhaps, to your interests is the use of ethylene bromide, $C_2H_4Br_2$, with tetraethyl lead, $(C_2H_5)_4Pb$, in anti-knock fuel, "ethyl gas" if you will. About two cubic centimeters of ethylene bromide per gallon of gasoline furnishes enough bromide to change the lead set free in the explosion into $PbBr_2$, thus keeping the lead away from the contact points. The growing popularity of "ethyl gas" has led to the installation of plants in Texas and North Carolina to extract bromine from sea water. Over 700,000,000 gallons of sea water are daily treated with chlorine and a little acid to drive out the bromine. Since a single cubic mile contains 600,000 pounds of bromine there is no danger of exhaustion of raw materials. Our production soared to 90,000 tons in 1956.

X

BRIMSTONE OR
CORNERSTONE

OUR EARLY ancestors grimly placed "brimstone" where they thought it belonged, while modern chemists make this brimstone, or sulfur, the very cornerstone of chemical industry.

Since beds of sulfur were common in volcanic regions around the Mediterranean it is no new element, nor were the ancients unaware of the fact that it burns. Sicily has the richest deposits in the Old World, but our own in Louisiana and Texas now lead in production. Besides this free or elemental form of sulfur there is much of it chemically combined with iron ("fool's gold"), copper, zinc, lead (galena) and molybdenum as metallic sulfides, lead sulfide, PbS, for instance. Then there are natural deposits of sulfates of calcium ($CaSO_4$), barium ($BaSO_4$), and magnesium ($MgSO_4$), the first named being gypsum and the last our good friend Epsom salt.

To be quite personal we must remind you of the adage which, if not current in the market place, might well be for it is absolutely true: No sulfur, no muscle! In other words, protein is composed of nitrogen, hydrogen, oxygen, and sulfur, well combined. If you doubt it, smell a thoroughly aged egg and trace the hydrogen sulfide, H_2S, so convincingly present, back to a general breakdown of the heavy and complicated protein molecule.

Sicily once dominated the world's sulfur market, rising to a production of half a million tons in 1905. Then something unbelievable occurred. Herman Frasch, in Cleveland, contrary to the best traditions of the average chemistry student, seemed to find the dry list of properties of sulfur very interesting reading indeed. He became obsessed with the low melting point of this element, 114.5° Centigrade, only a little above the boiling point of water, as he kept saying to himself. Then in a flash of genius he saw his way clearly. He would drill a hole 500 or even 1000 feet down to the enormous sulfur beds known to exist in Louisiana, pump water at 170°

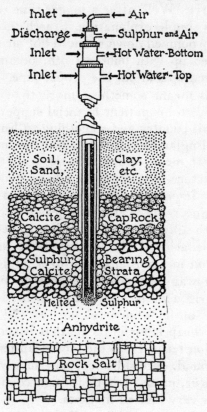

FIG. 28. A sulfur well.

Centigrade under sufficient pressure to raise the boiling point and keep the water liquid, and wait with confidence for the melted sulfur, free from dirt, to come up the inner pipe. He waited, still with confidence, several years, yet the sulfur, undoubtedly well melted down there, refused to come up.

Competent engineers at last discarded the idea as clever but impossible. One rashly offered to eat all the sulfur that

Frasch ever got out of his wells. This voracious gentleman lived to eat his words, if not the several million tons of sulfur that finally did pour out in a golden flood. Probably by this time you have guessed that of course sulfur being heavier than water couldn't rise. Well, after a longer time than it took you to think of this simple explanation, Frasch thought of it too, and straightway pumped down so much hot air that the melted sulfur, all puffed up with bubbly froth, became lighter than water, and flowed up and out the proper pipe.

This success meant something more than a reward to a good fighter and to his patient financial supporters—it meant something to this country and something to England. Early in World War I England implored us to make munitions faster and faster. That meant more sulfuric acid, the base of explosive manufacture, which we had been making from iron pyrites largely imported from Spain. Ships could not be spared and engineers were asked to design apparatus suitable for burning pure sulfur instead of pyrites to get sulfur dioxide for the sulfuric acid plants. It was done successfully and sulfur production in Louisiana rose to a million, two million tons. Although war demands have passed, much more than half our sulfuric acid is still made from domestic sulfur, largely because of its wonderful purity, 99.5 per cent.

In spite of cheap labor in Sicily, that island was forced to accept production terms from the American producers. Those holes in the ground, once ridiculed, now supply 83 per cent of the world's sulfur, much of it to foreign countries. Italy was allowed certain very limited markets.

Such a cheap raw material, easily stored in the open without loss, and produced in enormous quantities of high purity, is a great national asset. Since it is pure the sulfur dioxide obtained from burning it is pure enough to use in loosening the fibers of wood in paper making. Old-fashioned black gunpowder was a mixture of sulfur, charcoal, and saltpeter, but that explosive is no longer our only forceful chemical.

The farmer and fruit grower profit from sulfur for in the form of lime-sulfur spray or even as plain sulfur it holds in check dangerous scale and fungous enemies. Matches must contain it and some of our best black dyes are sulfur compounds. Without sulfur there would have been no rubber industry, or practically none, and the automobile would still be a dream. Pure rubber is a bit sticky in warm weather and brittle in cold, but in spite of that a certain Mr. McIntosh made the original "mackintosh" raincoat by smearing one side

FIG. 29. Rubber-coated clothing before Goodyear vulcanized rubber.

of a good Scotch plaid with sticky rubber and then pressing another cloth on this. Mr. McIntosh and his coat no longer adhered to the chair when he sat down in a warm room.

Fortunately for all of us an American inventor, Charles Goodyear, messing around on the kitchen stove, heated rubber and sulfur together with instant improvement. He had vulcanized rubber, back in 1839, had made a discovery that nearly a century later was to threaten the prosperity of railroads, to make the farm a suburb of the city, to revolutionize modern life.

Yet we were uneasy here in the United States about our

dependence upon the British and Dutch East Indies for rubber. We have the sulfur but we want to be sure of both essentials.

Since the United States bought 600,000 tons of raw rubber every year (half the world's production), while producing none, the British and Dutch once tried making us pay several

Goodyear Rubber Co.

FIG. 30. The rubber industry and, of course, the automobile industry had their beginnings in Mrs. Goodyear's kettle when Goodyear heated rubber with sulfur.

times the fair price of fifteen cents per pound. As a result old rubber scrap was worked over, rubber-producing plants studied carefully, and Neoprene invented. This flexible material is not chemically the same as rubber and costs more, but it is more oil-resistant and so has some special uses. We are assured that in an emergency Neoprene tires could be used successfully. Pure science, through the study of acetylene, gave us this safeguard against foreign monopoly.

Already some American companies are making different synthetic rubbers on a large commercial scale, and it is probable that in the near future they will greatly speed up production. We know how to become independent of the East Indies supply of natural rubber and we have the raw materials.

Neoprene rubber begins with acetylene (made from coal, limestone and water), while Vulcollan, Butyl rubber, GR-S and the others begin with substances prepared from petroleum. Natural rubber owes its useful properties to long chains of the isoprene unit, attached end to end. The butadiene unit from the petroleum refinery may also be built into elastic

Fig. 31. Tapping a rubber tree for latex.

chains by polymerization processes. Some of these synthetic rubbers make just as good tires as we now use and some have other valuable properties. The present cost is higher, but with large-scale production this margin will become small.

The true chemist is a hopeful philosopher, for he believes in turning even the worst of things to good account. Now there is that rotten-egg odor, never very well-liked, yet the chemist enjoys getting a quantity of it from better sources, and using it in analysis. Bubbled through water solutions of various metallic salts, it precipitates colored sulfides, some orange, some yellow, white, black, brown, and thus aids in the recognition of the different metals. There is really more to it than just that, but we do depend upon it for any broad scheme of analysis. Here is the simple way we represent the fact that hydrogen sulfide, H_2S, reacts with copper chloride, $CuCl_2$, to form hydrochloric acid, HCl, and black copper sulfide, CuS.

$$CuCl_2 + H_2S \rightarrow 2HCl + CuS.$$

Sulfur dioxide, that choking gas represented as SO_2, may not delight with its odor, but it does minister to your comfort in the household compression refrigerator. It is easily liquefied by the aid of an electric pump, but becomes heated in the process. How do we get effective cooling out of that operation? We could remove this heat of compression by a stream of city water but in small refrigerators air cooling serves. Valves automatically open at the right time and allow the cooled and compressed sulfur dioxide to expand. Since expansion of a gas requires energy from outside, heat from surrounding objects is absorbed with consequent cooling. On a larger scale ammonia is preferred to sulfur dioxide.

It would not be fair to ignore the contribution of this SO_2 to art, of a sort. By its inexpensive, although vigorous, bleaching aid, straw hats are changed from their natural yellow to the dazzling white so common in May, if not in August.

We seem to have assured you more than once that sulfuric acid is the king of acids. No doubt of it, for in this country alone 13,000,000 tons are made in a good year. Although not until 1765 was its manufacture really commercial, after that came demands for its use in bleaching, demands over a century later for huge quantities in petroleum refining, and still larger demands for the conversion of insoluble phosphate rock into super phosphate, available as plant food.

Until the last fifty years the acid was made only in a series of enormous lead "chambers" each containing 150,000 cubic feet, great mixing boxes for the gases. The process begins in a burner where sulfur, or a metallic sulfide, is roasted in a great draft of air.

$$S + O_2 \rightarrow SO_2.$$

Next the excess oxygen of the air is supposed to add on to the sulfur dioxide like this:

$$2SO_2 + O_2 \rightarrow 2SO_3,\ \text{sulfur trioxide,}$$

and then water vapor or spray is expected to unite with the sulfur trioxide to form sulfuric acid:

$$H_2O + SO_3 \rightarrow H_2SO_4,\ \text{sulfuric acid.}$$

Beautifully simple, but it doesn't work unless nitric oxide, a gas made from nitric acid, HNO_3, is present. The nitric oxide, NO, is a mere oxygen carrier because at the slightest opportunity it instantly seizes common oxygen of the air and forms nitrogen dioxide, NO_2.

$$2NO + O_2 \rightarrow 2NO_2,\ \text{nitrogen dioxide.}$$

Then this obliging nitrogen dioxide generously hands over half, only half, of its oxygen to the timid sulfur dioxide which doesn't seem to have the courage to seize the free oxygen of the air directly:

$$SO_2 + NO_2 \rightarrow NO + SO_3,\ \text{sulfur trioxide.}$$

As you now observe, the NO, nitric oxide, is ready to repeat its oxygen carrying. We call it a **catalyst** for the main reaction.

In more recent years we have learned to catalyze this great reaction in a few seconds by the Contact Process. A mixture of 93 per cent air and 7 per cent sulfur dioxide is rushed through a loose layer of dusty platinum supported on asbestos or other porous material, and maintained at the most favorable temperature, 400° Centigrade. If much hotter, the product is decomposed and money is lost; if much colder, the reaction is too slow. Somebody had to try a wide range of temperatures. In this process the catalyst is a solid, although a costly one. The reaction,

$$2SO_2 + O_2 \rightarrow 2SO_3,$$

goes on at great speed and is followed by the usual conversion of the sulfur trioxide to sulfuric acid with the aid of water. A promoted vanadium catalyst is now displacing platinum from this field.

Both processes continue with about equal tonnage, the Lead Chamber producing 70 per cent acid most cheaply and the Contact Process excelling with concentrated acid.

THE NEW SYNTHETIC RUBBERS

As a war result of our losing 97 per cent of our natural rubber when Japan captured the Dutch-British East Indies, we put great pressure on synthetic rubber development.

Copying Nature's trick in rubber, that of hooking together molecules of isoprene, C_5H_8, to form long, elastic chains or threads, the chemist used a related substance called butadiene, mixed with molecules or links of styrene, to form GR-S, our chief tire rubber, at least for 1956. This process of making big molecules out of little ones, especially in long chains, we call polymerization.

The invaluable butadiene is derived from certain petroleum products or from common alcohol, hence the conflict between farm interests and the petroleum companies. By January, 1957, we expect to be producing half a dozen synthetic rubbers at a total rate of 1,200,000 tons yearly, enough to take care of our vital military needs and those of civilians. The synthetics have great oil resistance.

SOME SYNTHETIC RUBBERS

Name	Monomer (Unit for polymerization)
Natural rubber	$CH_2 = C(CH_3) - CH = CH_2$, isoprene
Neoprene	$CH_2 = CCl - CH = CH_2$, chloroprene
GR-S	$CH_2 = CH - CH = CH_2$, butadiene, plus styrene
Butyl rubber	From petroleum units. Second class
Buna N	Butadiene plus $CH_2 = CH - CN$, vinyl cyanide

XI

THE GRAND PLAN

THE GREAT Russian chemist, Mendeleeff, insisted that it was a mistake to consider the elements as mere fragmentary, incidental facts in nature.

Over a century ago chemists began to look for some connection between properties and weights of the atoms but inaccuracies in the determination of some of those weights made progress difficult. Döbereiner in 1829 thought it curious that the atomic weight of bromine (79.9) is the average of the weights of chlorine (35.5) and iodine (126.9), especially curious because these three elements are remarkably alike in several properties. He found the same numerical relation in the "triad" group of sulfur, selenium, and tellurium where close chemical similarities are found, and in a third triad, calcium, strontium, and barium.

Döbereiner's triads were far from comprehensive but they provoked thought, led Newlands in England, thirty-four years later, to announce his "octaves," to suggest that if elements were set down in the order of increasing atomic weight, the eighth resembled the first in properties. Newlands' octaves contained the germ of a great idea, but he stopped too soon. Though ridiculed at the time, he enjoyed the satisfaction, twenty-one years later, of receiving the Davy medal from the Royal Society for his vision.

Mendeleeff, and independently Meyer in Germany, gave a far-reaching expression to the relations so dimly seen by Newlands. All the elements known in 1869 were placed in horizontal periods of seven, each one next heavier than the preceding. Putting hydrogen in a period of its own it was astonishing to note the similarities between elements in the same group or vertical column.

For example, lithium, Li, sodium, Na, potassium, K,

PERIODIC TABLE SHOWING ATOMIC NUMBERS IN HEAVY TYPE

PERIOD	GROUP 0	GROUP I	GROUP II	GROUP III	GROUP IV	GROUP V	GROUP VI	GROUP VII	GROUP VIII		
O		1 H 1.0080									
I	2 He 4.003	3 Li 6.940	4 Be 9.013	5 B 10.82	6 C 12.010	7 N 14.008	8 O 16.000	9 F 19.00			
II	10 Ne 20.183	11 Na 22.997	12 Mg 24.32	13 Al 26.98	14 Si 28.09	15 P 30.98	16 S 32.06	17 Cl 35.457			
III	18 A 39.944	19 K 39.10	20 Ca 40.08	21 Sc 44.96	22 Ti 47.9	23 V 50.95	24 Cr 52.01	25 Mn 54.93	26 Fe 55.85	27 Co 58.94	28 Ni 58.69
		29 Cu 63.54	30 Zn 65.38	31 Ga 69.72	32 Ge 72.60	33 As 74.91	34 Se 78.96	35 Br 79.916			
IV	36 Kr 83.8	37 Rb 85.48	38 Sr 87.63	39 Y 88.92	40 Zr 91.22	41 Nb 92.91	42 Mo 95.95	43 Tc 99	44 Ru 101.1	45 Rh 102.91	46 Pd 106.7
		47 Ag 107.880	48 Cd 112.41	49 In 114.76	50 Sn 118.70	51 Sb 121.76	52 Te 127.61	53 I 126.92			
V	54 Xe 131.3	55 Cs 132.91	56 Ba 137.36	57–71 Rare-Earths	72 Hf 178.6	73 Ta 180.95	74 W 183.92	75 Re 186.31	76 Os 190.2	77 Ir 192.2	78 Pt 195.23
		79 Au 197	80 Hg 200.61	81 Tl 204.39	82 Pb 207.21	83 Bi 209.00	84 Po 210.0	85 At 210			
VI	86 Ra 222.0	87 Fr 223	88 Ra 226.05	89 Ac 227	90 Th 232.05	91 Pa 231	92 U 238.07				

Actinide Series. 93 Np, 94 Pu, 95 Am, 96 Cm, 97 Bk, 98 Cf, 99 E, 100 Fm, 101 Mv caesium, Cs, and rubidium, Rb, in Group I are all rather light metals which react violently with water to yield hydrogen gas and a strong base or alkali such as NaOH or KOH. Nor can it be any accident that barium, Ba, calcium, Ca, and strontium, Sr, fall together in Group II. All three are metals reacting mildly with cold water to form hydrogen and rather mild bases. Fluorine, chlorine, bromine, and iodine resemble each other so much that they are called the Halogen Family—and you find them in Group VII.

Not all the groupings are so happy and in some instances each group must be divided into two sub-groups to justify the arrangement. Mendeleeff showed his mental power by occasionally leaving gaps, placing the next heavier element farther to the right where its chemical and physical properties placed it. He felt certain that these gaps would be filled by elements yet to be discovered, and they were. He lived to see three of them added to his table with atomic weight, density, and other properties remarkably close to values he predicted. We forgot to mention that atoms of elements in Group I can hold just one atom of chlorine ("valence" of one), atoms of elements in Group II can hold two atoms of chlorine, in Group III three atoms of chlorine, in Group IV four atoms of chlorine, etc. Elements at the left form powerful bases, alkalies; elements at the extreme right form strong acids; those in the middle weak bases or weak acids.

You see there is a convincing sweep to the thing, and there is really much more to be told.

But you are asking the meaning of Group O. That wasn't Mendeleeff's work for he had no helium, argon, etc., to trouble him. It was Sir William Ramsay who got us into that difficulty—and also got us out, very handsomely for all concerned. He discovered the absolutely inert gas argon about 1895 and helped Lord Rayleigh discover the equally lazy helium (on this planet, at least). To dispose of such elements Ramsay invented Group O, which permitted him to stick to the idea of writing down elements in the order of their atomic weights although it made the periods contain eight instead of seven elements and forced the arrangement of a few "long" periods of fifteen. The name, Group O, was a happy one signifying zero valence, or combining power, since helium and argon are too lazy to combine with any atom.

Ramsay must have had imagination in addition to his many other delightful qualities for his speculative eye at once noted new gaps in the table, gaps in his own Group O. He fearlessly accepted the challenge and sought the "missing links" where he found argon, in the air, liquid air, to be exact.

FIG. 32. Russian stamp honoring Mendeleeff.

He got them—neon, Ne, krypton, Kr, and Xenon, Xe, and so joined the ranks of "Chemistry's Immortals," that exclusive company of men who discovered elements.

As you see already Mendeleeff's Grand Plan led to the discovery of new elements, helped to show that some atomic weights were wrong because some elements at first were thrown in with strange bedfellows, classified facts, and stimulated research in general.

However, your critical eye has already noticed that if the order of increasing atomic weights was followed, argon would be in Group I and potassium, K, in Group O. But would you have taken violent potassium away from its kin, alike as, not two, but several peas, and put it with the lazy helium and neon? No, that, and divorcing argon from its lazy friends, would outrage your sense of the fitness of things. Perhaps you saw, also, that tellurium, Te, and iodine, I, were reversed from their weight order, so that they might rest appropriately and peacefully in the bosoms of their respective families.

These two glaring defects were to be wiped out in 1914 when Moseley, the brilliant young English physicist, later killed at Gallipoli, developed the more fundamental system of atomic numbers. He measured the wave lengths of X-rays thrown off from different metals used as anti-cathodes or "targets" in an evacuated X-ray tube. These X-rays, by passage through a crystal, were separated into bands of different wave lengths something like the solar spectrum but invisible. However, they showed their pattern on a photographic plate, permitting Moseley to calculate the wave length coming from targets of copper, gold, iron, etc. The heavier the metal the shorter the wave length. How thrilled this young genius must have been to discover a simple numerical relation between the wave lengths of the most intense lines in the different X-ray spectra!

Moseley expressed this relation in a series of values which he called **atomic numbers,** strangely enough, all whole numbers beginning with hydrogen, the lightest element, as one. It turned out that these numbers were identical with the number of free protons (positive charges) in the nucleus of each atom. For example the atomic number of potassium is 19 which means not only that it is the nineteenth element in order of increasing weight but also that there are nineteen free protons in its atomic nucleus.

Now with the argon-potassium order set right, not to mention the tellurium-iodine order, we agree that *the chemical properties of the elements are a periodic function of their atomic numbers.*

Six elements were discovered in a period of thirteen years. Number 72, called hafnium after the city of Copenhagen, was discovered in 1923 by Coster and Hevesey. Numbers 43 and 75 were isolated in 1925 and 1926 at the University of Berlin by Noddack and named masurium and rhenium. With the discovery of illinium by our own American chemist, B. S. Hopkins, at the University of Illinois in 1926, this country entered the lists. Hopkins reasoned from Moseley's table of atomic numbers that the missing No. 61 must resemble the other members of that curious group, "the rare earths," found in monozite sand. He predicted that it must fit in between neodymium and samarium and looked for it in their crystalline salts as a friendly impurity. None was separated but finally new lines and absorption bands both in the visible and X-ray spectra appeared with increasing concentration of the impurity desired.

Hopkins' discovery left two existing elements to be discovered as indicated by two gaps in the table of atomic numbers. The United States has apparently made a strong finish after a belated start by adding No. 87 in 1930 and No. 85 in 1931. Papish at Cornell University claims the first by use of the same X-ray spectrum method that aided Hopkins. Allison and Murphy at Alabama Polytechnic quite independently made the same discovery of 87 with a tool devised long ago by Faraday but not hitherto used in discovering elements.

The plane of vibration of light polarized by passage through a crystal of Iceland spar is twisted or rotated as it passes through a transparent substance placed between the poles of a powerful magnet. However, there is a lag or delay of about one billionth of a second after switching on the magnet, before the optical rotation is observed. Since this lag differs with different elements, the apparatus may be used to detect traces. In fact Allison and his associates went on from discovery of No. 87, which must resemble sodium, Na, and potassium, K, to capture the last element-at-large, No. 85, which must resemble iodine. So delicate is their method that their most concentrated source of No. 85 contained only one part in a billion. As is the way with scientists the identification of elements 87 and 85 must be repeated by several other workers of unquestioned ability before final acceptance.

Although only ninety-two elements occur in nature, man's efforts to break up the nucleus of certain atoms and to build it up to heavier mass in some others have added nine more, all heavier than uranium, except one.

So the time-honored list has very recently had these startling additions, thanks to Hahn, Fermi, Seaborg and others Two of these new elements play a role in atomic power.

Element	Atomic Number	Symbol	Atomic Weight
Neptunium	93	Np	237
Plutonium	94	Pu	242
Americium	95	Am	243
Curium	96	Cm	245
Berkelium	97	Bk	247
Californium	98	Cf	249
Einsteinium	99	E	254
Fermium	100	Fm	255
Mendelevium	101	Mv	256

XII

THE FALL OF THE HOUSE OF URANIUM

A MORE scientific Edgar Allan Poe might well have written of the dramatic fate of the heaviest of all elements, uranium, rather than the Fall of the House of Usher. Yet Poe had no such choice, for the world never even dreamed of the meteoric career of uranium until Crookes' work with the high-vacuum electric discharge tube in 1878 led to Röntgen's discovery of X-rays in 1895 and this in turn to Madame Curie's discovery of radium in 1898.

How marvelously were events linked together. Without the foundation of Crookes' work we should today have no X-ray tubes, no revealing system of Atomic Numbers, no knowledge of the inner structure of the atom, no radium with its healing influence, no merciful extension of the surgeon's vision by X-ray photography of the human body, no radio, no great triumph of successful television and only inadequate knowledge of the inner atomic groupings of solids.

With this sense of the far-reaching importance of the discovery of electric discharges through high-vacuum tubes we may take a lively interest in their construction. Sir William Crookes forced a high-voltage current into the tube through a sealed-in wire at A, the anode, and out by another wire, the cathode, sealed in at C (Fig. 33). A rarefied gas is a good conductor of electricity no matter what fantastic shape may be given the containing vacuum tube.

Crookes observed a greenish-yellow fluorescence of the glass end of the tube, directly opposite the cathode, caused by mysterious rays proceeding in straight lines from the cathode. They could not be mere light rays, he felt sure, because they were deflected in a magnetic field.

Here the puzzled Crookes handed on the torch to Sir

J. J. Thomson, brilliant young physicist at Cambridge University, destined to be the scientific father of an imposing galaxy of new stars. Thomson finally decided that he had enough experimental evidence to inform the Royal Society (1897) that "cathode" rays are streams of flying particles of negative electricity.

They were ponderable pellets of a sort for they heated a piece of metal placed in their path as a "target" and they were negatively charged because deflected in the appropriate direction by a magnet. His conclusion was that these flying corpuscles or "electrons" must be constituents of all matter,

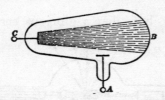

FIG. 33. A high-vacuum tube showing
cathode rays.

for no matter what the gas in the partial vacuum or what the materials of the tube, the cathode rays were always the same.

One of the few types of bricks that make up the atom was discovered. Another was to be captured years later by Rutherford, Thomson's most brilliant pupil. As a final *tour de force,* the great master determined very nearly the correct mass (a better term than weight) of the invisible electron, although Millikan in the United States was later to surpass his accuracy by the ingenious oil-drop experiment.

We have gotten ahead of our story for in 1895 there came together that potent pair, a fortunate accident and a keen, logical observer. Röntgen, Austrian physicist, quite by chance left near a Crookes tube a photographic plate, well covered with black paper. Later, by another fortunate accident, this plate was developed with others. We can imagine that the plate recorded the shadow image of a bunch of keys or heavy metallic object resting on it. At any rate it recorded the effect of rays which Röntgen remembered must have penetrated the opaque wrapping. Of course, like a true scientist he repeated the experiment, successfully, as you now know. The mysterious penetrating radiations from the Crookes tube he named "X-rays."

Becquerel in France was haunted by the fancy that the fluorescence of the glass at the end of the Crookes tubes, now to be called X-ray tubes, was connected with the invisible radiations. Acting upon the theory that any fluorescent or phosphorescent substance must also give off X-rays he placed many such solids upon photographic plates covered with black paper.

He was wrong, but what a glorious error he made. Only

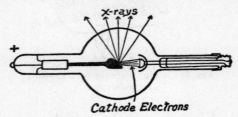

FIG. 34. An X-ray tube.

one solid, a uranium compound, had any effect on the plates. Once more note the operation of a well-oiled, scientific mind. Becquerel repeated the experiment with other uranium salts and minerals—they all radiated penetrating rays.

Furthermore these rays from uranium (Becquerel rays, as they were temporarily named) discharged the leaves of the electroscope, a new scientific tool destined to play a useful rôle in the field of radioactivity. This electroscope is a very simple contrivance of a metal rod insulated from a glass bottle or flask by a rubber stopper and terminating in a strip of thin gold foil or leaf attached at one end but, for most of the length of the gold leaf, free to move away from the metal rod.

When charged by touching the rod with a stick of hard rubber which had been rubbed along some rough cloth the gold leaf moved away from the rod because leaf and rod had received like charges of electricity, and like charges repel.

Discharge of this electroscope by a uranium salt held near but not touching the metal rod must be due to something flying off from uranium and making the air a conductor. Becquerel observed that this effect was proportional to the uranium content of salts but with pitchblende was great out of all proportion to the amount of uranium present. The generous Becquerel, suspecting that this unexpectedly great effect was due to a new and strange element in the pitch-

FIG. 35. The electroscope.

blende, suggested to Madame Curie that she attempt to isolate it.

Marie and her talented husband, Pierre, with painstaking care and some privations, struggled for two years, separating into all its constituents the ton of pitchblende kindly donated by the Austrian government. Every compound removed was tested for Becquerel rays by use of the invaluable electroscope. The results were discouraging until the bismuth fraction or residue was tested. Common bismuth showed no activity but this bismuth which had "lived in the presence of the best," with uranium, for thousands or millions of years had become royal—it discharged the leaves of the electroscope three hundred times as rapidly as uranium alone.

Madame Curie reasoned that the bismuth residue must have dragged down with it a new element of unprecedented activity. She separated it from the bismuth and named it polonium in honor of her native land, Poland.

This triumph came in 1898 and was quickly followed by a greater—the isolation of a radium compound from the barium residues, taken from pitchblende. This wonder-element was at least 3,000,000 times as active, as radioactive, as uranium. First obtained in combination as radium bromide, it was not until twelve years later that Madame Curie completed her epochal work by isolating radium itself. Like barium, calcium, and strontium, of its own family, radium proved to be a metal, silvery but tarnishing quickly in the air, reacting gently with water to evolve hydrogen and taking its place in the column of the Periodic Table occupied by barium, calcium, and strontium.

Twice awarded the Nobel Prize, elected to succeed her husband as Professor of Physics at the Sorbonne, twice given a gram of the costly radium by citizens of the United States, honored by kings, presidents, and the greatest scientists, Marie Sladowska Curie, simple and unassuming, will forever hold a unique place in history. Yet, like Faraday, she had first been engaged to wash dishes in a great laboratory.

As soon as she announced her great gift to humanity, able research workers all over the world were attracted by the new problems latent in radium. J. J. Thomson at Cambridge proved the identity of the beta rays from radium with the cathode rays or streams of electrons of the X-ray tube.

Rutherford in Montreal placed a speck of radium salt near a mass of phosphorescent zinc sulfide in a small tube with adjustable lens attached (the spinthariscope). In the dark he saw sparks flashing where some sort of particles flying out from the radium bombarded the zinc sulfide, one flash for each particle. He called these alpha particles and counted the number emanating from a known weight of radium in a given time. Soddy in England actually collected these flying particles and calculated their weight for they, like the streams of negative electrons, could be deflected in a magnetic field, in the opposite direction, however. "Proof positive" that alpha particles were positively charged.

Almost unbelievable to the world was the news that Ramsay and Soddy had proved the alpha rays to be streams of positively charged helium atoms. What a blow to the time-honored definition of an element! But just the same, radium is an element for its smallest units with the properties of radium are distinct entities and take part in chemical reactions like the atoms of stable elements.

A third radiation from radium, polonium, and mesothorium, the gamma rays, was soon recognized as practically identical with X-rays. Since they are waves, not streams of negative or positive particles, they are obviously not to be deflected in a magnetic field. A bit of radium in the bottom of a deep lead tube open at the top sends out all three rays but if enclosed in a magnetic field only the gamma rays emerge. The others are bent against the walls of the tube and absorbed.

RADIUM RADIATIONS

Alpha rays	Positive particles	Helium atoms	20,000 miles per second	Stopped by 0.1 mm. aluminum
Beta rays	Negative particles	Electrons	180,000 miles per second	Stopped by 4 mm. aluminum
Gamma rays	No charge	X-rays		Stopped by 1 foot iron

Rutherford, drawing a gentle stream of air over radium and through a tube cooled by liquid air, captured and condensed a mysterious gas which by itself discharged an electroscope, was radioactive, but which in less than one week of radiant existence or wild extravagance, as you prefer, died of exhaustion. Here was another new element, radon, quite obviously unsuited for museum shelves.

Try your best to explain Rutherford's great experiment with the simple apparatus shown in Fig. 36. Inserted in the glass tube B were spark electrodes above and a thin-walled glass tube A below. B was evacuated and tube A filled with helium gas under very slight pressure for the walls of A were less than 0.01 millimeter in thickness. No spectroscopic evidence of helium in B could be found during spark discharges between the two wires. The walls of A were good, although thin, since no gas leaked through.

Now for the climax. Radium emanation, or radon, was admitted to A and spectroscopic testing of the spark discharge in C begun. After a few hours the spectrum of helium in C was observed.

There could be only one explanation. Helium gas molecules in the usual gaseous motion failed to penetrate the walls of tube A yet the unstable radon shot its own decomposition

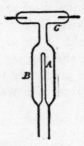

FIG. 36. The first definite proof of the transmutation of elements.

product of charged helium atoms through the glass at 20,000 miles per second initial velocity. Here is unmistakable proof of the transmutation of an element, so long desired by the alchemists.

To pile proof upon proof let us show you C. T. R. Wilson's ingenious fog track apparatus, now made available at small cost for any laboratory. The glass vessel A (Fig. 37) is a sort of inverted ink bottle nearly, but not quite, filled with ink or black water for effective contrast. To the neck of the bottle is attached a rubber bulb, B. By squeezing B the black water is forced higher, compressing the enclosed air. The heat of compression is carried away by the water, etc. Now let go of the bulb, very quickly. Of course the water falls and the air, saturated with moisture, cools with expansion. All the conditions for fog formation are right except one—there are present neither dust particles nor electrically charged gas molecules to act as nuclei for condensation of water molecules into visible droplets.

Wilson had a brilliant idea. Why not charge the air by aid of alpha particles flying from a mere fragment of radium? So a pin-point bit of a radium salt was placed at one side of the air space at the top of the apparatus. Now at each com-

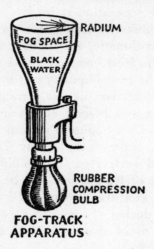

FIG. 37. This apparatus sweeps away your skepticism about radium.

pression and quick release of the bulb a dozen or more straight white lines are seen to flash out from the point of radium. What could they be but rows of water droplets condensing around ionized or charged molecules of air. Passage of a single helium atom smashing at 20,000 miles per second through thousands of air molecules, knocking outer electrons out of atoms, guarantees formation of charged nuclei.

Now we have prepared you, adequately we hope, for a real shock. Uranium, the heaviest element, throws off three helium atoms and two electrons (one at a time) to become radium, taking plenty of time to do it, maybe a billion years. Freeing a uranium salt from the omnipresent radium reduces the activity of uranium, not to zero but to a low point; but this pure uranium slowly recovers its radioactivity, forms more radium. The radium in turn ejects violently more negative electrons, more positive helium atoms, and dies. The corpse is lead with an atomic weight of 206. The helium atom weighs exactly 4, and uranium exactly 238. Loss of enough helium 4's reduces 238 to the 226 of radium and, finally, to the 206 of lead. The Fall of the House of Uranium has been complete—the final generation is lead.

For fear you think the lead coffin was dragged in by a mere process of arithmetic we shall remind you that the atomic weight of the lead impurity found in uranium ores is 206 while that of the lead impurity in thorium ores is 208.4. Thorium is also radioactive, decays through a series of steps by loss of electrons and helium atoms into lead but a successive subtraction of six helium 4's from 232.12, the atomic weight of thorium, leaves very nearly 208.4 weight of an atom of this second variety of lead. This puzzling existence of different weights of lead atoms will be discussed in a few minutes. Doubtless you are also puzzled by our indifference to weight changes during the escape of electrons. They are mere trifles with a mass of only 1/1837 that of a hydrogen atom.

So by counting the particles of helium thrown off in a given time by a definite weight of radium we know that half of any sample of radium you may happen to own will have decayed, disappeared, in about 1590 years. You can well believe that all the radium in the world today is younger than the human race.

The age of the earth can be calculated from the amount of helium gas accumulated in uranium minerals, for laboratory experiments show that one gram of radium in one year gives off 167 cubic millimeters. By this method scientists are now convinced that the earth is approximately 2,000 million years old—like the iron meteorites. The sun and stars, however, are older. "If the age of a human being is 1 second, of the human race 6 hours, then the lower limit of the age of

the earth is 1 year, and the age of the stars 5,000 years."
(*Hevesy.*)

The radiations from radium are powerful in other ways
than in penetrating solids. One gram gives off more than
enough heat every hour to melt its weight in ice, to be exact,
132 calories. As you remember, its flying particles make zinc
sulfide luminous, hence its use on the face of "radiolite"
watches. Glass is colored, gems put through their color paces,

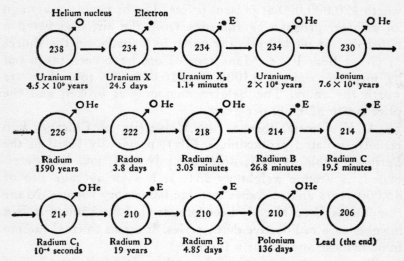

Fig. 38. Early table of decay steps. Half life.

and cloth disintegrated if placed near a radium compound.
What, then, would happen to a man who carried around a
gram in his vest pocket? It would be the death of him, unless
he encased it in a heavy lead box.

Curiously enough radium "burns" on the flesh may develop into cancer yet we use it to check the growth of surface
cancers. Rather we use tubes of the radium emanation
(radon) which is daily drawn from the main supply kept in
the safe. We might as well use this gas, for in a week it is
worthless.

So rare is radium that it once sold for $120,000 per gram,
although it later fell to $100,000 when the Colorado-Utah

carnotite ores were utilized, and to $70,000 or less after the discovery of extraordinarily rich ores in the Belgian Congo (1922). One gram of radium is obtained from nine tons of Congo ore as compared with one from 400 tons of the United States ore.

Up to 1929 the world had produced only 300 grams, not enough for medical use, but by 1941 total production had reached 800 grams or nearly one pound and three-quarters, worth $20,000,000 at present prices. Ten or twenty years ago an aviator, prospecting for ores from the air, discovered a rich ledge of pitchblende far north in Canada, on the shores of Great Bear Lake. Many tons of ore have been taken out by airplane and, at $5000 or $10,000 per ton, they are worth the effort. The Belgian monopoly is broken and the price cut to $20,000 per gram.

A. V. Grosse, then at the University of Chicago, had recently isolated protactinium (Pa), previously listed in the Periodic Table as U-X, or element No. 91, and had determined its atomic weight as 231. It has an average life of 46,000 years and so comes into the laboratory for use. Many compounds have already been prepared. Like radium it is a member of a radioactive decay series. It seems to rival radium in occurrence and so has a future.

The treatment of cancer by radium is rivalled by use of modern X-ray tubes but that competition exists only for surface cancers. The recent tremendous power given to these tubes is appalling. For instance the 1,200,000 volt Coolidge hot-cathode tube recently made for the Miller Hospital in St. Paul can shoot out rays more potent than all the radium the world has ever seen. A $75,000 tube equalling $100,-000,000 worth of radium! Now radioactive cobalt-60, by-product of atomic power plants, supersedes radium.

Useful and sensational as the discovery of radioactivity has been, its great importance lies in its revelation of the structure of the atom.

We have already told of Thomson's discovery of the electron in the cathode rays of an X-ray tube and in the beta rays from radium—a constituent of all matter as he put it. Several years later his former pupil, Rutherford, discovered another constituent of the atoms, the proton, by directing a stream of charged helium atoms from radium against sodium, aluminum, and phosphorus. In each case charged hydrogen atoms, detected by the spectroscope, were smashed out of the atomic nucleus of these heavier elements. Now the positively charged hydrogen atom (or ion) is merely a hydrogen atom that has lost its lone electron, in other words is the nucleus, the lightest one in the world. Rutherford named this building brick of the atoms, proton.

With all this great accumulation of evidence we feel certain now that the atom is a miniature solar system, mostly space with practically all the mass concentrated in a relatively minute nucleus, a nucleus that contains all the protons and neutrons (neutral particles of proton weight). The electrons needed to balance electrically the positive protons are planetary electrons, rotating in elliptical orbits around the nucleus. The simplest atom is hydrogen with a single electron rotating around a ring proton. The next heavier is helium with a pair of electrons rotating around a nucleus containing two protons and two neutrons. Uranium is very complex, with 92 protons, 146 neutrons and 92 electrons arranged in all sorts of layers. As a rule it is the outermost electrons that shift from atom to atom in chemical reactions or are shared in pairs by atoms reacting to form molecules of new substances.

The ease with which alpha particles from radium smash through gas molecules (or metal foil) and continue in straight lines as observed in the fog track apparatus, convinces us of this very open structure of atoms. Harkins took 20,000 photographs of fog tracks before securing one that showed a fork or Y caused by a heavy helium atom actually hitting a solid nucleus and bouncing off at an angle.

The modern theory of atomic structure explains the difference in weight of the lead from uranium and the lead from thorium. They are alike chemically because their outer layers of electrons, which do the reacting, are the same but they have different weights because they have different numbers of heavy protons and neutrons in the nucleus.

Such different weight forms of an element, isotopes as they are called, may be well illustrated by drawings of the two isotopes of chlorine. One has an atomic weight of 35 and the other of 37. Mixed as they are in common chlorine gas the average atomic weight is 35.46.

Aston proved that many elements have isotopic forms by comparing their weights with an accuracy of 1 part in 10,000, using the mass spectrograph. He passed the positively

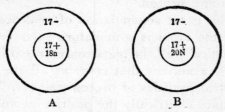

FIG. 39. Isotopes of chlorine.

charged gas molecules going in the direction opposite to the negative cathode rays of an X-ray tube between the poles of a powerful magnet, and on to a photographic plate. These flying gas molecules are bent out of their straight-line course by the magnetic field. If all have the same mass or atomic weight, they all focus on the same line on the plate but if the element used has atoms of different weights their magnetic deflections are different and a series of parallel lines show on the plate. Calculation shows the relative weights most convincingly.

Neon, the first gas tested, showed that 90 per cent of its atoms had a weight of 20 and only 10 per cent a weight of 22. Naturally the average weight must be 20.2, a calculation in perfect agreement with its atomic weight as determined by other methods.

About 1930 it was found that oxygen was not a simple element of mass 16 but was a mixture of such atoms with a relatively very small quantity of oxygen atoms of masses 17 and 18.

The conception of the proton, or hydrogen atom stripped of its one electron, as a building brick of other atoms is hard to explain when we attempt to show that a helium atom weighing exactly 4 was created from four hydrogen nuclei, each of which weighs 1.008. Many scientists believe that the loss of mass required here was manifested in the form of radiant energy—a transformation of matter into energy. If so, the radiation of energy from the sun corresponds to a loss of mass of 4,000,000 tons per second. Other scientists postulate an annihilation of protons and electrons in the terrifically hot center of the sun. This would account for vastly greater amounts of solar energy radiation and promise us a far greater life of the sun.

"If we could transmute the hydrogen in a tumbler of water into helium," said Aston, "the energy obtained could drive the *Mauretania* across the Atlantic and back."

Aston's dream has been realized and submarines are now propelled by atomic energy. In a decade or less great power plants will utilize such energy and ultimately we will be free from dependence on coal as fuel.

XIII

ATOM SMASHING

NUCLEAR CHEMISTRY has opened up a fascinating field of research—research that is revealing the secrets of the atom and may have profound importance in the war on cancer.

Planetary electrons are readily stripped from atoms by heat, ultra-violet light and the current-passage through a Crookes tube. In the last instance the stripped atoms of any gas present drive through a canal in the cathode, becoming positive rays (not to be confused with negative cathode rays of electrons going in opposite direction). But to force ejection of particles from the nucleus is far more difficult, although spontaneous with the unstable nuclei of radium, mesothorium, protactinium and their like.

It was Rutherford, in 1919, who first succeeded in the artificial disintegration of an element, nitrogen, by bombardment with alpha rays (high-speed helium nuclei). In rapid succession he knocked protons (hydrogen nuclei) out of a dozen elements by the same technique.

Discovery of the neutron in 1932, by Chadwick of Cambridge University, was one of the sensational results of such nuclear attack, bringing the Nobel Prize to its discoverer. From the beryllium atom, shaken and shattered by swift alpha particles from polonium, came a radiation of incredible penetrating power, not stopped by several feet of lead. These speeding particles from the beryllium nucleus were electrically neutral, hence neither attracted nor repelled by charged units in the atoms of matter. Harkins believes that it would take a million *million* neutrons to fill up the space occupied by an average atom.

America scored about the same time in discovering the positron, the positive mate of the negative electron, the same in mass but opposite in charge. Anderson, at California Institute of Technology, in 1932, secured many photographs of fog tracks of positrons thrown out when cosmic rays disrupted certain atoms. Electrons were also thrown out but, due to the strong magnetic field, curved in the opposite direction. The life of a positron is a fraction of a second for it is

FIG. 40. Fog tracks of alpha particles from radioactive elements crashing through nitrogen. One direct hit on a nitrogen nucleus is shown. Harkins.

converted into energy as it collides with an electron, each annihilating the other.

Slow neutrons were discovered by Fermi, the Italian, who observed that activation was enormously increased in the passage of high-speed neutrons through paraffin, water, or any compound rich in hydrogen. Other substances had little or no effect. These slower neutrons are more readily captured by the nuclei of certain elements such as hydrogen.

In this sensational nuclear warfare every conceivable type of bullet was tried, in several instances with brilliant success.

BULLETS FOR ATOM-SMASHING

Alpha particles.—Nuclei or charged hearts of helium atoms spontaneously thrown off at high velocity by radium, polonium, mesothorium and other radioactive elements. At this moment workers are firing "bullets" from synchrotrons with billions of electron-volt force.

Electrons.—The beta particles ejected from radioactive elements, from heated substances, and from the cathode of X-ray tubes. Not heavy enough to compete with the others.

Protons.—Hydrogen nuclei, or charged hearts, formed

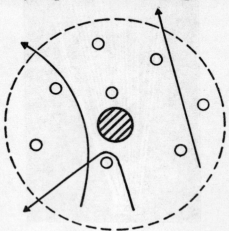

FIG. 41. Positive alpha particles passing through the open structure of an atom may be uninterrupted if relatively far from the positive nucleus, deflected if near and reflected back if about to collide with the nucleus.

from hydrogen during passage of an electric discharge through a vacuum tube and given high velocity as "canal rays" passing through a hole or canal in the cathode. Other gases in such a tube may be ionized and driven through the cathode canal as positive rays.

Neutrons.—Penetrating neutral particles (of proton weight) ejected from beryllium and certain other elements during bombardment by alpha particles. Neutron rays are said to be more effective biologically than X-rays.

Deuterons.—Nuclei or hearts of deuterium, heavy hydrogen atoms, consisting of two protons and one electron or, by more recent theory, a proton and a neutron in the nucleus, with one planetary electron.

ATOM-SMASHING APPARATUS

The most common device for accelerating the atomic bullets is a giant X-ray tube producing positive rays (canal rays) of any desired gas. Even with high vacuum there is some gas in the tube and its atoms become ionized. Tubes operating at a million volts and much higher are now in use.

Lawrence and his associates at the University of California invented the first powerful gun, a whirligig electrical machine in which gaseous ions are given an accelerating tap during rotation by reversing the polarity of a 220-ton magnet, later to be replaced by a 5000-ton magnet. Speeds corresponding to 11,000,000 volts were obtained with the startling report that Lawrence had succeeded in shooting alpha particles (four times the weight of a proton and twice the weight of a deuteron) through air in a luminous beam. Even with deuterons he converted platinum into gold. The biologic possibilities are startling, for Lawrence's cyclotron had sent out a beam of bullets clear of the machine for a distance of five feet.

Speeding alpha particles, protons, or deuterons, are probably captured by the nucleus before emission of other units. In a way it may be supposed that the new nucleus formed by addition of a proton or other particle is unstable and must break down into a stable nucleus, by means of emission of energy or particles.

TRANSMUTATIONS

Bombardment by heavy deuterium nuclei, as expected, has proved to be more effective than smashing with hydrogen nuclei of half the weight. For example lithium has been transmuted into helium ions or alpha particles by overloading the nucleus so that it breaks apart. The atomic weights are indicated in the equation below.

$$\text{Li} + \text{D} \rightarrow 2\text{He} + \text{Neutron}$$
$$7 \quad\ \ 2 \qquad\ 8 \qquad\quad\ 1$$

Lawrence at the University of California (1933) forced neutrons out of beryllium by impact with 3,000,000-volt deuterons. Previously this had been done in Europe by use of alpha particle bullets. To date not only beryllium but helium, lithium, carbon, argon, nitrogen and oxygen have yielded neutrons under bombardment. It must be a building brick in atoms.

Lauritsen and his associates at California Institute of Technology used deuterons in an attack on beryllium. Boron was the product of transmutation in this instance.

$$\underset{9}{Be} + \underset{2}{D} \rightarrow \underset{10}{B} + \underset{1}{Neutron}$$

The expected attack on nuclei by the 25,000,000,000-volt synchrotron, now being built at a cost of many millions at Brookhaven National Laboratory, will be exciting.

Artificial Radioactivity and Cancer

Artificial radioactivity was first produced (1933) by Irene Curie and her husband, Joliot, by bombardment of boron with alpha particles. The disintegration of boron continued for 15 minutes or longer after the bombardment stopped. With bombarded aluminum the decay period was four minutes.

It is true that Cockroft and Walton, and others, a year previously had forced a dozen non-radioactive elements to throw out alpha particles during bombardment with high-speed protons. However, such radioactivity stopped with the end of the attack.

This extremely important research has been continued in several laboratories with such success that "induced radio-activity" has been produced in more than sixty chemical elements. The course of their compounds may be traced through the animal body.

A most promising achievement, from the standpoint of cancer treatment, may well be the production of radioactive sodium by Lawrence who bombarded common salt with 1,750,000-volt deuterons. The remarkable thing is that this radioactivity continued after bombardment ceased with a half-life of 15 hours. The gamma rays from such radioactive sodium are twice as powerful as those from thorium C. If this radioactive salt were used in the animal body it could not continue indefinitely and dangerously, like radium salts, to attack tissues. High-velocity beams of alpha particles or deuterons are also being used with interesting results on animal cancers.

ATOMIC POWER. URANIUM FISSION

In 1939 and 1940 the atomic "fission" of the uranium isotope of mass 235 was recognized both in Europe and in America. Neutrons from radium bombardment of beryllium were slowed down by passage through such hydrogen compounds as water or paraffin so that they were effectively captured by the U-235 nucleus with a resulting sensational splitting into barium and krypton or other elements not differing greatly in mass. This fission was accompanied by a tremendous gain in energy, nearly 200,000,000 electron volts per atom of U-235. Compare this impressive figure with the two or three electron volts of energy released by burning an atom of carbon or of hydrogen.

There is an important chain of reactions in fission in the sense that secondary neutrons are released to cause other fissions and, theoretically, to continue until all the U-235 in a given sample is exhausted. However, the presence of U-238 and other impurities quickly breaks this chain reaction. Since U-235 is only one part in 140 of common uranium, the critical problem is separation to obtain pure U-235. A more detailed account of the atomic bombs and atomic power will be given in the last chapter.

It was rumored that Hitler placed every possible resource at the disposal of his scientists in the hope of obtaining power, explosive or industrial, from uranium fission. It is also a fact that this is an official war project in our own country.

XIV

THE ROMANCE OF
THE LAZY ELEMENTS

IN THE chapter on The Grand Plan you read that one thing led to another, that the discovery of lazy argon persuaded Ramsay of the existence of other elements like it. But how did it all start, what led scientists to suspect the existence of argon?

It began with Cavendish, contemporary of Priestley and Lavoïsier, when in 1785 he decided to take air apart, just to "see what made it tick." Easy enough to wash out the usual dust and London smoke, to catch the carbon dioxide with any base such as "caustic soda," to dry the gases and even to remove the oxygen with the aid of hot carbon or copper, but nitrogen, accounting for four fifths of the total volume, was not much inclined to react with other substances. At last the peculiar but able Cavendish hit upon the idea of admitting extra oxygen to the tube containing the indifferent nitrogen and passing a stream of electric sparks from wire to wire through the mixture. Not because of any magic but because of the high temperature of the spark the two elements united to form oxides of nitrogen. These acidic gases were seized by their arch enemy, a basic solution at the bottom of the tube. With adequate drying no gas at all should have been left in the tube.

Every time Cavendish tried the experiment there remained an obstinate gas residue, not much to be sure, only about 1/120 of the original air. Strangely enough he did nothing with this gas except to mention it in his notes. He had a bird, a genuine *rara avis,* in his hands and let it fly away. This was argon, giving promise of a better entrance on the laboratory stage a century later.

Prophecy was fulfilled in 1895 when Lord Rayleigh, great

British physicist, took everything out of some air except the nitrogen, and weighed the nitrogen. It was distinctly heavier than the unquestionably pure nitrogen prepared by decomposing ammonium nitrite. Ramsay, the chemist, was called in to suggest a suitable substance for reaction with the nitrogen. They passed the extra-heavy nitrogen over hot magnesium which captured the nitrogen (as magnesium nitride) and allowed the suspected impurity to pass on. Remarkably enough the remaining gas was about one per cent of the original volume of the air, just as Cavendish had noted over a century earlier.

Ramsay and Rayleigh were not careless, they put the new gas to every test and found it the first element on record to refuse to react with anything under any conditions. No wonder they named it argon from the Greek word for "lazy." Plentiful enough, when you consider that the air above one acre weighs 40,000 tons of which nearly one per cent is argon. Its very inertness was finally capitalized in filling millions of the larger tungsten lamps with argon and in excluding air in welding certain metals.

More important, however, was the creation of a new column, Group O, in the Periodic Table of the elements, forced upon science by this supremely indifferent stranger. Ramsay reasoned that there must be more lazy elements to fill in the new gaps in the expanded table and began to search for them as for a needle in a haystack.

His first clue was a remote one. During the solar eclipse of 1868, Lockyer and Janssen had made spectroscopic observations of the sun's chromosphere and found certain new lines not belonging to any known element. Quite appropriately they named the distant element helium, from the Greek, *"helios,"* the sun.

The next clue was fresher. The American chemist, Hillebrand, analyzing a uranium mineral, uraninite, released a gas imprisoned in the rock when he dissolved the mineral in acids. He thought it was probably nitrogen left over from entrapped air after the oxygen had reacted with other elements.

Poor Hillebrand! He too, like Cavendish, just missed a chemical immortality for he had entertained a distinguished guest, helium, and failed to recognize it. When Ramsay began his search some thoughtful friend called his attention to Hillebrand's experiment. Ramsay bought a gram of another uranium mineral, cleveite, for three shillings sixpence and proceeded to release a gas by disintegrating the rock with acids. To the amazement of the scientific world the spectral lines of this gas were identical with those of the helium in the sun. In the brief space of two months Ramsay had discovered an element, found it on the earth's doorstep after its discovery in sun and stars.

How strange that eight years later Ramsay and Soddy were to show that helium was formed by atomic disintegration of radium, itself the child of uranium. No wonder it was enclosed in uranium minerals where it had been accumulating for millions of years.

There was very little helium to work with, more of it secured from certain spring waters than from uranium rocks, yet it was soon shown to be absolutely and satisfactorily lazy, lazy enough to join argon in Group O of the Periodic Table. Apparently it defied all efforts to convert the gas to liquid, bid fair to stand apart as the only gas never conquered. Then came Kammerlingh Onnes at the University of Leyden with a super-cooling technique that broke all records. The last gas collapsed and in 1908 helium became a clear liquid just 4° Centigrade above the absolute zero where molecules supposedly cease to move. It was not until 1926 that this chilly liquid was frozen to a solid under 28 atmospheres pressure and within a single degree of absolute zero. Some chemical Alexander may well sigh for something else to freeze. All substances have now been frozen to solids.

A news note of April, 1931, quite properly made much of the announcement that "Washington last week caught up with Leyden, Toronto, and Berlin in the matter of liquefying helium." At the U. S. Bureau of Standards they chilled compressed hydrogen by surrounding it with liquid air; allowed the hydrogen to expand, thus cooling the rest of it to a still lower temperature; compressed the super-cooled hydrogen until it liquefied; allowed this liquid hydrogen to evaporate at reduced pressure around a tube of highly compressed and chilled helium; secured liquid helium. Each evaporation produced a lower temperature. It was a long fight with more details than can be enumerated here. In the liquefier the helium flows through a series of coils of metal tubing sus-

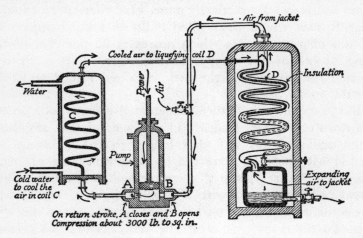

FIG. 42. Air-liquefying apparatus.

pended inside a succession of metal cases and vacuum jacketed vessels to prevent loss of "refrigeration."

At such low temperatures, near absolute zero, some metals such as tin and lead and mercury lose all their resistance to a current of electricity yet others like gold, copper, and silver are not greatly improved in conductance.

Following the example of Onnes, a startling demonstration of this property of super-conductance was used by McLennan to entertain the Royal Institution in London. "I exhibited to the audience a closed ring of lead immersed in liquid helium and carrying a current of more than 200 amperes. The current had been started (by induction) in the super-conducting lead ring some six hours earlier in the afternoon by Prof. Keesom in Leyden, and it persisted undiminished in intensity while being transported by aeroplane to London."

Up to 1914 helium was a useless sensation in spite of its unique properties. Even had they known then that the gas conducts heat six times as well as air and carries a spark ten times as far as oxygen there would have been no applications of such knowledge for the excellent reason that there was no helium to use; well, practically none. Had there been enough, Great Britain would have filled balloons and airships with this non-inflammable gas which possesses 92 per cent of the lifting power of the dangerous hydrogen. The earth was searched for helium and the little obtained valued at $2500 per cubic foot.

In the meantime, Nature perpetrated a great joke on the little town of Dexter, Kansas. The citizens of that ambitious village drilled a gas well that loudly roared a promise of great industries to be attracted to Dexter because of cheap natural gas. Other "gassers" were triumphantly blown in and a great celebration held with the formal lighting of a gas jet before the assembled crowd as the climax of the day—or night. To the disgust of crestfallen citizens the gas refused to burn. That was in 1903. The joke reached the ears of Cady and McFarland at the State University and resulted in their analyzing the gas. No wonder it failed to burn for it was 80 per cent nitrogen.

With a scientific intuition or "hunch" to spur him on, Cady took the gas apart and finally had a thimbleful of a light, lazy gas that turned out to be helium. Several years passed until at a national meeting of the American Chemical Society held in Kansas City in 1916 a paper was read by one of Cady's associates listing the composition of natural gas from different wells in Kansas. Suddenly R. B. Moore of the Bureau of Mines, a former pupil of Ramsay, leaped to his feet and with suppressed excitement read a letter from Ramsay asking if a source of helium could be found in the United States because Great Britain desperately needed it to replace the dangerously inflammable hydrogen in military balloons and airships. Here was the answer to prayer, in Kansas. Helium was now to move swiftly from the joke of Dexter to the tragedy of war.

Through Moore's efforts an Army and Navy Helium Board was organized with the Bureau of Mines and private companies coöperating. Texas gas fields were selected for development and by the end of the War 200,000 cubic feet, compressed in strong steel cylinders, awaited shipment at New Orleans. At the previous price of $2500 per cubic foot this first instalment of helium was worth a tidy fortune. Separation of the helium from the natural gas depended upon the fact that all the other gases are comparatively easy to liquefy while helium is extraordinarily difficult to condense.

The Texas gas at Amarillo contains 1.75 per cent helium, which is rich in comparison with gas in Canada (about 0.3 per cent) and other countries. Recently a Colorado gas showed the phenomenal content of 6 per cent helium. No other country with the possible exception of Canada owns any considerable amount of this great military asset. Incendiary bullets cannot ignite giant dirigibles filled with helium. For that matter airships in times of peace are made far safer by use of this gas. It is no small achievement that our government plant can now produce 500,000,000 cubic feet each year at a cost of less than one cent per cubic foot. We need plenty, for giant dirigibles may require 6,500,000 cubic feet to fill them. Our reserves promise to last a century.

Sir William Ramsay was not content with the placing of argon and helium in a special column of the Periodic Table devoted to laziness. He suspected that since argon was found in the air he might discover others like it in the same mixture. Again he used liquid air as a convenient raw material and, by separating fractions of it as they evaporated, concentrated three more lazy elements—finally separated them as neon, krypton, and xenon.

Ramsay did not live to see the great use of neon-filled advertising tubes that give our city streets a rosy glow at night. These tubes, twisted into the shape of letters, are really almost vacuum tubes containing neon at the very low pressure of five or ten millimeters.

AIR CONTAINS, BY VOLUME

Nitrogen		78.04%
Oxygen		20.99%
Argon		0.94%
Hydrogen	1 part in	8,000
Neon	1 part in	80,000
Helium	1 part in	250,000
Krypton	1 part in	1,000,000
Xenon	1 part in	11,000,000

A far-sighted company is ready to furnish krypton, separated from liquid air, for research in order to find uses for it. Undoubtedly a use will ultimately be discovered.

To secure one pound of neon 44 tons of liquid air are required, 725 tons for one pound of helium, 173 tons for one pound of krypton, and 1208 tons for one pound of zenon.

The inert or lazy gases of the argon group have refused so far to form compounds, in fact they have but one atom in the gaseous molecule. However, evidence has been offered by H. S. Booth at Western Reserve University of the formation of a fluorine compound of argon.

XV

FED FROM THE AIR

WHEN THE Hebrew prophet Elijah, hiding in the mountains from his enemies, was literally "fed from the air" by kindly ravens, he little thought that by the twentieth century, A.D., the human race would recognize the atmosphere as an ultimate source of food. Nitrogen in some available form we have long known as absolutely essential to plant growth but the problem has been to "fix" air nitrogen, to convert it into soluble compounds acceptable to growing plants. There is no lack of "free" nitrogen, free as air, for 20,000,000 tons of this gas rest on every square mile of earth.

True, the nitrifying bacteria attached to the roots of clover, alfalfa, and other legumes, have always possessed the secret of nitrogen fixation. Such crops enrich the soil when plowed under and have a great place in crop rotation. But their method baffles us. Then for nearly a century Chile saltpeter or sodium nitrate, $NaNO_3$, has extended our fertilizer resources, by a great total of 55,000,000 tons. What a joke that the first shipload of this available nitrogen went to England as mere ballast with scarcely a thought of any market for it. England later was glad to pay well for Chile saltpeter. The wheat farmer was once prodigal in the use of the guano, or bird manure, from the islands off the west coast of South America but that reserve is gone now—millions of tons of it. So will the vast deposit of Chile saltpeter go, although not as soon as feared by the great British physicist, Sir William Crookes.

In 1898 he challenged the chemist, in effect, to save the race. "The fixation of nitrogen is vital to the progress of civilized humanity. Unless we can class it among the certainties to come, the great Caucasian race will cease to be the

135

foremost in the world, and will be squeezed out of existence by the races to whom wheat or bread is not the staff of life."

Crookes had reasons for his gloomy forebodings. In the century from 1800 to 1900 the world's population had doubled, an appalling rate of increase that could only result in partial starvation, and wars for food. The chemist accepted the implied challenge and drove back the specter of starvation for the race to a far distant horizon. His, rather than the aviator's, was the real conquest of the air. Not satisfied with a single method of "fixing" the atmospheric nitrogen in forms available for plants and useful to man, he sought for and found a second and a third process, each better than the previous.

The first victory, as momentous as one of Napoleon's most glorious triumphs, came in 1903 when Berkeland and Eyde, the Norwegians, emulated the lightning flash. They blew air through a roaring electric arc distended to a six foot disk at 3000° C., and in the wink of an eye, forced the nitrogen and oxygen of the air into combination, as nitric oxide, NO. On cooling, another atom of oxygen readily adds on to yield red-brown fumes of nitrogen dioxide, NO_2. This gas, blown up through a tower down which water splashes, reacts with the water to form the valuable nitric acid—and a by-product, nitric oxide. But you remember that this colorless nitric oxide always adds on oxygen, if it gets a fair chance, to form nitrogen dioxide which, we have pointed out, is as good as nitric acid when wet.

Spectacular though this "arc process" is, its requirements of electric power are too great for competition with later processes of nitrogen fixation. It has passed out everywhere except in Norway and is dying there. We still benefit by the lightning flash which is hot enough to compel marriage of nitrogen and oxygen. Rain washes from the air the oxides of nitrogen formed, to the extent of 1,500,000,000 tons of available nitrogen on the globe per year, if we accept the estimates of the great Arrhenius.

The next conquest of the air is credited to two Germans,

Caro and Frank, who coupled atmospheric nitrogen to calcium carbide, CaC_2, forming calcium cyanamide, $CaCN_2$, useful as a fertilizer and source of ammonia. Not until 1906 was their discovery put to commercial use. You perhaps know that coke and lime, CaO, heated in the electric furnace, yield calcium carbide, famous as a source of acetylene gas, if moistened with water. Then if nitrogen (not air) is passed over the calcium carbide at 1100° C. reaction (2) takes place and nitrogen has been fixed.

(1) $3C + CaO \rightarrow CO + CaC_2$, calcium carbide,
(2) $CaC_2 + N_2 \rightarrow C + CaCN_2$, cyanamide,
(3) $CaCN_2 + 3H_2O \rightarrow CaCO_3 + 2NH_3$, ammonia.

The great Muscle Shoals cyanamide plant (No. 2) was built during World War I to secure quick results, for there was already in operation at Niagara Falls a company understanding the process. News leaked out of Germany of a superior but difficult process of direct union of nitrogen and hydrogen to form ammonia and we put our research men on the problem. But research can not always be hurried with guaranteed results so we played safe with the old standby, cyanamide. It was planned to steam the cyanamide, reaction (3) above, to get ammonia and to unite this with sulfuric acid to form the great fertilizer, ammonium sulfate, or to oxidize it into nitric acid so essential to the manufacture of high explosives. Although costing many millions of dollars and run only long enough to test the plant, the Muscle Shoals No. 2 plant was worth the cost as a threat to the enemy. For twenty years it was continually in the limelight as a bone of contention in Congress. Meanwhile water ran over the great Wilson Dam at Muscle Shoals to no profit. World War II brought it into full use, for another process and for general power. The cyanamide process has been pushed to the wall by the far better Haber process which requires no great amount of power. Cyanamide manufacturers held on tenaciously but they will always occupy a minor place in the competition.

One of the greatest triumphs of chemical engineering was

Haber's success in Germany, 1913, in uniting the elements, hydrogen and nitrogen, by main force to yield ammonia. "Main force" is the right phrase for the reaction took place in alloy-steel bombs built like cannon, operating under 3000 pounds pressure and at 500° C. temperature. At such temperatures and pressures hydrogen badly weakened common steel, so chrome steel free from carbon was used.

Nor was this all. Only in the coaxing presence of a catalyst, essentially a porous mass of iron "promoted" with some such materials as the oxides of aluminum and potassium

FIG. 43.—Mighty steel cylinders, cannon-like, are needed for some of the modern high-pressure reactions of chemical industry.

could the nitrogen and hydrogen be persuaded to unite. Terribly difficult and dangerous at every step was the process yet it made Germany in her hour, no, her four years of need, independent of Chile saltpeter. Without the Haber success, perfected just in time, Germany would have run out of ammunition within less than a year.

The vast military importance of the simple reaction,

$$N_2 + 3H_2 \rightarrow 2NH_3, \text{ ammonia,}$$

becomes plain to you when we call attention to Ostwald's earlier discovery that a mixture of air and ammonia passed through a platinum gauze at 600° C. and above yields oxides of nitrogen in less than 0.01 second. This put ammonia in the list of munitions of war.

(1) $4NH_3 + 5O_2 \rightarrow 6H_2O + 4NO$, nitric oxide,
(2) $2NO + O_2 \rightarrow 2NO_2$, nitrogen dioxide,
(3) $3NO_2 + H_2O \rightarrow NO + 2HNO_3$, nitric acid.

As you see from equation (3) possession of the red-brown nitrogen dioxide is as good as possession of nitric acid. Nitric acid is needed to make high explosives, even the smokeless powder of rifles. Germany carried on although denied sea lanes to Chile. Before 1913 the whole world made its nitric acid by treating Chile saltpeter, sodium nitrate, with concentrated sulfuric acid.

$$2NaNO_3 + H_2SO_4 \rightarrow Na_2SO_4 + 2HNO_3.$$

Now, by a quick change of practise, this method has become obsolete and all of our nitric acid is made by oxidation of ammonia.

In later years "direct fixation" of nitrogen as ammonia by the Haber process finally dominated the scene. Of the 1939 world production of over 2,000,000 tons of available nitrogen, less than 10 per cent was supplied by Chile saltpeter, 18 per cent by coke ovens, 10 per cent by the cyanamide and 60 per cent by the synthetic ammonia process. Production was actually being limited by agreement between some of the nations to check ruinous price-cutting. For a time Germany led in fixation processes, but now it is probable that we have the greatest capacity. Our War Department's earlier estimate of 144,000 tons of fixed nitrogen for a year of major warfare had to be revised in the light of the tremendous demands of World War II. By 1956 we will "fix" 4,000,000 tons of atmospheric nitrogen yearly, most of it for fertilizer. Great amounts of compressed ammonia gas are now released directly into soils.

In the decade after the war, our vast capacity for manufacture of ammonia and nitric acid was well utilized, in part, to make ammonium nitrate, a fertilizer of unusually high nitrogen content. Since it cakes badly on storage, some treatment must be devised to keep it granular for safe and convenient handling. The economic status of farmers on overworked land can be raised by cheaper fertilizers.

The nitrogen required of course comes from the air, but the production of the pure hydrogen needed is more of a problem. Water gas, prepared by steaming white-hot coke, is one present source in America. A later source of hydrogen is the catalyzed reaction between steam and the methane of natural gas.

XVI

HIGH EXPLOSIVE— THE LIBERATOR

A GREAT Roman aqueduct built by the Emperor Claudius had to be carried through Monte Solviano by a tunnel, three and a half miles in length. What was that to the most powerful ruler in the world with innumerable slaves to do his bidding? Yet today a competent American engineer actually controls more power than the Roman despot ever had. Claudius had to wait eleven years for 30,000 slaves, toiling underground, to lead that tunnel five feet a day, while a modern engineer with a hundred men and tons of dynamite could do it comfortably in ten months. Those tons of dynamite liberated an army of toiling slaves.

How were the 6,000,000 tons of huge stones in the Great Pyramids of Egypt quarried? By the incredible toil of thousands of slaves equipped only with bronze picks and wooden wedges to be swollen with water. We may well marvel at the skill and infinite patience of the leaders in this great task but we know that the followers simply endured. Need we call attention to the drudgery of 300,000 men building the Great Wall of China or of 80,000 Hebrews working for seven years in King Solomon's quarries?

Dynamite, with its mighty heart of nitroglycerine, has freed these slaves, accomplished tasks impossible even to a million toilers.

And yet when explosives are mentioned, the first thought in the mind of the average citizen is war, made frightful by smokeless powder, "T.N.T.," picric acid, and the rest. The chief use of high explosives is not for war but for peace, liberating mankind. During the entire four years of World War I the Allied forces used approximately two billion pounds, no more than the United States alone used from 1926 to 1930 for the arts of peace.

One third of our 300-500 million pounds per year is used in coal-mining, a fifth in loosening ores from the solid grip of old Nature, and a sixth of the imposing total in rock quarrying. A hundred million pounds tear tunnels through mountains, lead railways through rough country, remove hidden

Barber Asphalt Co.

FIG. 44. Today rock is quarried with high explosives, not by slaves.

rocks from harbors, excavate for foundations of great skyscrapers, loosen rock for the construction of roads and dams. Twenty million pounds clear stumps from land desired for farms, loosen the hardpan and rock where fruit trees are to be planted, create drainage ditches at small cost, and open up river jams of logs or ice.

Much of this work simply would not be done if expensive human or animal labor were the only force available. Power, intensely concentrated in high explosives, is cheap power. Iron and copper, for example, would necessarily cost much more if their ores could not be economically loosened in readiness for handling with a steam shovel. Raw materials for our concrete roads, such as limestone and cement rocks, were quarried so cheaply by dynamite slaves that the vast network of solid highways was made possible.

Although black gunpowder, a mixture of charcoal, sulfur and saltpeter (potassium nitrate), has been known a long time, certainly since the time of Roger Bacon the learned monk and since 1346 when Edward III defeated Philip of France at Crecy with the help of gunpowder and wooden cannon, it was the discovery of a process of making **nitroglycerine** in 1847 by the Italian, Sobrero, that gave man the key to limitless explosive power. And then for two decades the world used his nitroglycerine only as a heart stimulant!

It was twenty years before Alfred Nobel, the Swedish inventor, made Sobrero's process practical and five years more before he mixed the highly temperamental liquid with an inert, porous clay ("kieselguhr") to make the safer **dynamite.** When you speak of "beating swords into ploughshares" think of the Nobel fortune yielding rich income for the Nobel Peace Prize.

It is almost too easy to make, this nitroglycerine, a mere matter of mixing ordinary glycerine, a by-product of soap-making, with concentrated nitric and sulfuric acids. Of course if you happen to be the workman operating a nitrator producing 3000 pounds in one batch your interest in seeing that cold brine circulates through the cooling coils to keep the temperature below the explosive point, becomes somewhat more than academic. Since too rapid mixing of the raw materials piles up the heat of reaction it is a safe bet that you will add the glycerine slowly, oh, very slowly, to the acids. After the nitroglycerine has risen to the top (in about an hour and a half) it is drawn off, very gently to be sure, and washed free from acids. This explosive liquid is the best thing ever invented for "shooting" oil wells but it cannot safely be transported on trains.

For general use, then, it must be "gentled" with wood meal (now replacing kieselguhr), sodium nitrate, ammonium nitrate, and other powdered solids which take up the liquid. The fillers now used in this dynamite add to the volume of gases formed by explosion. Impatient miners years ago occasionally thawed out frozen dynamite in order to start the day's work earlier during severe winter weather. Quite often they started more than they planned, explosions resulted. By the application of sound scientific principles manufacturers learned to dissolve in the nitroglycerine other nitrated products to lower the freezing point sufficiently for very cold weather. Quarries need 60,000,000 pounds of dynamite yearly.

To modify the shattering action of this tremendously brusque explosive ammonium nitrate, NH_4NO_3, has been substituted for part of the nitroglycerine, resulting in a heaving action on rocks, quite important where fine fragments are not required.

Nobel greatly extended the usefulness of his nitroglycerine by discovering that it dissolves enough nitrocotton to form a jelly on standing, a product known as gelatin dynamite. With this sensitive jelly, quivering would probably be completely without merit.

It is only another easy step from gelatin dynamite to cordite, the smokeless powder used by the British army during World War I. Acetone, a colorless liquid, once made only by the destructive distillation of wood, is used to dissolve the mixture of nitroglycerine and nitrocotton (and a little petroleum jelly). The pasty mass is forced through dies, cut into suitable lengths, and allowed to dry into translucent, horny masses. A favorite and perfectly harmless amusement fancied by young chemists is the carving of finger rings out of the great inch-thick grains designed for huge cannon. Think of whittling a lump of this powerful explosive and then calmly setting fire to it! A quick puff—and you are still there, intact. But when detonated with a percussion cap, whose fulminate of mercury explodes with almost infinite velocity, the smoke-less powder exerts itself to the utmost.

So limited was the world's production of acetone early in World War I that when the British ordered 24,000,000 lbs. of cordite from the United States it was stipulated that huge quantities of acetone be delivered with the cordite. The order was filled although a vast quick-vinegar plant had to be built for production of the acetic acid which could be readily converted into acetone, and a seaweed harvesting and distillation industry had to be developed on the California coast.

FIG. 45. "Give us acetone," cried the Allies, "or we are lost."

The most popular high explosive in war, speaking for the sender and not for the receiver, was "T.N.T.," trinitro-toluene. Toluene, a colorless liquid by-product of the coke oven, readily reacts with concentrated nitric acid to yield a mighty solid that seems to stand train wrecks very well indeed but, set off by percussion cap in a shell or mine or torpedo, can explode with devastating fury. The Allies couldn't get enough of it until they discovered that it could be adulterated with cheap, easily made ammonium nitrate with no loss in power. "Amatol," they called the mixture.

There seems to be no limit to this power of nitric acid to impart dangerously explosive properties to various substances. Not merely glycerine and cotton waste or pure wood cellulose, but starch, can be nitrated. And then what a devil of a fellow it becomes! Even the sweet and gentle sugar when nitrated in a mixture with glycerine, develops as nasty a disposition as

FIG. 46. You don't have to prove that T.N.T. is trinitrotoluene.

any of them. Carbolic acid ("phenol"), never a social favorite, becomes a dangerous associate after nitration—picric acid, they call it then.

It seems inconsistent to speak of some explosives as too sensitive but deliberate efforts are made to tone down some of them. Some are beyond taming, like the fulminates suitable only for use in the minute quantities needed in percussion caps. Nitrogen triiodide, so easily made that it is wiser to keep you in ignorance of the method, is safe enough wet but after drying, is detonated by the footsteps of a large and restive fly.

Odd, too, to talk of "safety explosives" for coal mines but they have saved thousands of lives. Old-fashioned black gunpowder flashed so much flame that coal dust or mine gas was often set off with disastrous consequences. Now chemicals may be added to dynamite to "cool" the flame, shorten it in length and time, with practically no danger of initiating a general mine explosion.

The bursting effect of these powders and dynamites is due to the sudden release (by chemical reaction) of enormous quantities of gases, further expanded by the great heat of the reactions. Simple but sudden chemistry.

Back of it all is Nitric Acid, or its salts. There is scarcely a high explosive used today that is not a nitrated product.

As a 1941 postscript to this chapter we should remark that the toluene from coal distillation is quite inadequate to meet our needs for T.N.T. in a major war. Already we are building plants to prepare toluene in great quantities from petroleum products. Petroleum chemistry gives us fuels and lubricants and can give us explosives, synthetic rubber, glycerine and other important substances.

As a 1956 postscript: The maximum annual yield from coke ovens was never more than 30,000,000 gallons. Latest war needs call for about ten times this much. One gallon of toluene can be nitrated to yield ten pounds of T.N.T. The chemist came to the rescue by devising a method of converting a certain petroleum fraction into toluene. Petroleum chemistry gives us fuels and lubricants and can give us explosives, synthetic rubber, glycerine and other important substances.

RDX, derived from ammonia and formaldehyde, was used against tanks and for destruction of bridges. But the atomic bomb is now supreme as a devastating high explosive.

XVII

SILKS AND CELLULOSE

THE REQUIREMENTS for evening dress for Cave Men—and Women—did not go beyond animal skins and a few red berries strung together like beads. In warmer climates grass skirts were more adequate. Then came Industry, ruining the simple life. Wool and cotton were fabricated, taste developed that required fabric for tents, sails for ships, rugs and blankets for the tribal chiefs.

Then one fine day, according to Chinese legend, a little princess dropped a silk cocoon into her cup of hot tea and found that the tough silken coat could be unrolled into a strong, slender fiber. Silk had arrived to clothe royalty, to be sold for its weight in gold, to be the cause of many violent deaths. Silk culture was an important industry as early as 3000 B.C. Exportation of the little silk-worms, or even the eggs, from China was forbidden on penalty of death. But European princes coveted the precious fabric and finally managed to smuggle the eggs out of Asia. Venice stole the secret in 1203; King Henry of Navarre spent great sums developing silkworm-growing in France; and Elizabeth I dared to be the first in England to entrust her legs to silken hose.

Today Japan produces most of the raw silk of the world and has made production an art and a science. In China production is still primitive. The delicate yet gluttonous little worms must be fed every two hours a ration of mulberry leaves. Some 30,000 silkworms eat 1700 pounds of the fresh leaves and, in return, spin just 12 pounds of silk.

And what a fiber it is! As strong as an iron wire of equal diameter, delicate, beautiful, comfortable. The waxy coating, sericin, about one quarter the weight of raw silk, must be cooked off with a hot soap bath. To restore this weight, and a little more, silk is "weighted" with tin salts.

The fastest ships afloat were none too fast to rush their precious cargoes of Japanese silk across the Pacific, and none but trains with absolute right-of-way carried the fabrics from Seattle to New York. A trainload worth a million dollars was so tempting to thieves that insurance rates were boosted to a thousand dollars a day, armed guards properly placed. This great annual importation of Japanese silk, 75,000,000 pounds worth over $400,000,000 in good years although cut

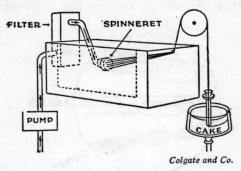

Colgate and Co.

FIG. 47. Rayon solution forced through many small holes in a platinum disk (spinneret), coagulated as threads in an acid bath and spun into lustrous fiber.

drastically at present, was a restraining power in international affairs. We have a substitute for the silk but Japan has no substitute for the $400,000,000, or even the $100,000,000 of depressed years. Has anyone yet called *Bombyx mori,* the best of the silkworms, a member of the United Nations? Worse selections have been made.

Long ago royalty lost the exclusive right to adorn its person with this lustrous fabric but its cost kept it out of the reach of the middle class, not to mention the poor. Cotton had to serve the masses. A short lifetime ago their craving for realizable beauty of fabric seemed about to be gratified with mercerized cotton, cotton given luster of a sort by a process of soaking in caustic soda and stretching so as to cause an untwisting of the fibers.

But something vastly better was in sight. In 1884 Count Hilaire de Chardonnet of Besançon invented the first silkworm robot. Forcing a solution of nitrated cotton in alcohol-ether (the collodion of today) through very small holes in a solid "spinneret" he secured silky threads as the volatile solvents evaporated in warm air. Garments woven from these twisted threads of cellulose nitrate were lustrous, prized for beauty, until it was learned that an entire dress could burn in a fraction of a second to the shame of lady, chemist, et al. Obviously the nitrate groups ($-NO_3$) in the new molecules furnished plenty of internal oxygen for combustion. The re-

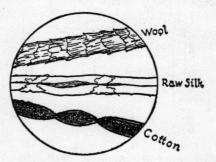

FIG. 48. Fibers of wool, raw silk, cotton.

sourceful chemist then proceeded to denitrate the fibers by immersion in a suitable bath hoping that luster would not be lost. He won, for the product, though chemically brought back to the original cellulose of cotton, still looked and felt like silk.

Now you are wondering what this chemical called cellulose really is. Just $(C_6H_{10}O_5)_x$, if that means anything to you. At any rate you can see from this empirical formula that the molecule contains many atoms of carbon, hydrogen, and oxygen—more than at first appears, for the "x" after the formula stands for an uncertain number multiplying the basic formula.

You eat cellulose fibers with your celery, lettuce, and most vegetable food to no digestive profit except as "roughage" aids digestion. Cattle secrete more potent juices for they are able to assimilate some of the modified cellulose of hay. Some bacteria are known to attack these resistant molecules. Several years ago it was found that sawdust cooked under pressure with dilute acids was partly converted into sugars and other digestible material. The hope was expressed that this discovery bid fair to double the pasture lands for cattle, in effect, by utilizing wood waste from the forest. The discovery was somewhat in advance of its time. These sugars could be fermented into alcohol, grain alcohol, but at present other sources are cheaper. However, it is good to have such knowledge in reserve.

This huge cellulose molecule must have some moderately reactive groups of atoms or it could not be nitrated. It has at least three hydroxyl groups (— OH) and these are the points of attack not only by concentrated nitric acid but by caustic soda with carbon disulfide, as the artificial silk industry proves. Skip the following equation if you wish, although it describes in brief the making of the high explosive, guncotton.

$$C_6H_7O_2(OH)_3 + 3HNO_3 \rightarrow 3H_2O + C_6H_7O_2(NO_3)_3.$$

Count those (— NO_3) groups, three of them, and deny if you will, that "cellulose trinitrate" is a good descriptive name for guncotton, wrongly called by the public "nitrocotton." A less vigorous nitration introduces only one or two nitrate groups and yields a milder product, mixture of the dinitrate and mononitrate. This is the stuff that Chardonnet dissolved in alcohol-ether and spun into silk.

By this time you are anticipating us and asking why we do not use other acids, acetic perhaps, to exchange acetate groups for the (—OH) groups of cellulose. You are quite right, clever too, for that has been done to make cellulose acetate silk. Well, not by direct treatment with strong acetic acid alone, but by its derivative, acetic anhydride. Such a silk does not need to be decomposed back into the original cellulose like Chardonnet's cellulose nitrate for it burns very slowly. It is a better silk, growing rapidly in favor and production at the present moment. Its wet strength is much greater than that of the other rayons.

Yet even these are not enough. Far surpassing both in production is viscose silk, made by attacking cellulose of cotton, or purified wood fiber, with caustic soda and the evil-smelling carbon disulfide. The orange-colored stuff resulting is "cellulose xanthate," if you care to know, but you would not care for a dress of it. It too, like cellulose nitrate, must be dissolved in liquid, spun, decomposed (in an acid bath) to yield the original cellulose, fortunately still lustrous.

Four fifths of our production of rayon, now accepted as the proper name for all artificial silks, is viscose yarn but cellulose acetate is rapidly gaining, now that cheaper acetic acid has arrived. Cuprammonium silk, or Bemberg yarn, made by dissolving cotton in a solution of ammonia and copper oxide and forcing the liquid through spinnerets into an acid, accounts for only a small fraction of the total and yet it has its special merits. Finer even than natural silk fibers, only 0.004 of an inch in diameter, a filament 4225 miles in length would weigh only one pound.

World production of rayon is probably over 3,000,000,000 pounds, with nearly a third of the fast-growing total made in the United States. At first its luster was too obtrusive but now it is dulled or delustered by various devices and is growing rapidly in popularity with no limit in sight. Since rayon takes dyes differently from natural silk, attractive color or shade effects result when a fabric of mixed rayon and silk is dyed. In the manufacture of feminine underwear the three textiles, nylon, rayon, and cotton divide the field, with nylon leading.

The lower nitrated forms of cellulose exert a great influence on modern life in a very different way. Mixed with camphor to form a tough transparent film, long known as celluloid, it becomes the very foundation of the vast "movie" industry, not to mention amateur photography. Unfortunately in this product the cellulose nitrate is not denitrated and made safe like the present type of Chardonnet rayon. Hence the fire-proof movie booth and high insurance rates as well as annoying restrictions on the use of current movies and talkies in schools.

The safe, but somewhat more expensive, cellulose acetate

form of celluloid film requires no fireproof booth, offers no fire hazard anywhere. The amateur's film is of this type and all of it should be. An official report of the Cleveland Clinic disaster states that six tons of exposed X-ray films stored in the basement were ignited by inexcusable contact with a 100-watt Mazda lamp. This almost explosive fire giving off 125 pounds of prussic acid gas (HCN), and poisonous oxides of nitrogen, causing the death of 124 persons, could not have

Fig. 49. Cotton bolls, the raw material for rayon, explosives, photographic film, auto lacquers, and other useful products.

occurred had cellulose acetate film been used. Law makers need to inform themselves as to the relative costs and merits of the two types of transparent film. The devastating Baltimore fire of 1903 with its loss of $100,000,000 has been attributed to storage in one wholesale house of a dangerous supply of old-fashioned celluloid collars. Possibly this was only a humorous slander on Baltimore, or was it aimed at the now-extinct race of men who once choked themselves with those glazed monstrosities?

Another transparent film, **cellophane,** has recently enjoyed a meteoric rise to popular favor as an attractive and protective wrapping for foodstuffs, shirts, and all sorts of articles. In its water-proofed form it prevents the drying out of most materials. It is our friend viscose rayon, chemically cellulose, in film rather than filament form, used in this country to the extent of 100,000,000 pounds yearly. Ingenuity went pretty far in shaping this clean and harmless film into sausage casings, but success was immediate.

Fig. 50. The wasp was the first paper maker.

Cellulose nitrate dissolved in various mixed solvents, some of them very recent industrial creations, appears as a lacquer, vigorously competing with paints and varnishes. Automobile bodies are more handsome and better with "Duco" lacquer than they ever were with paint. Interesting to note that until manufacturers learned how to reduce the viscosity of these lacquers they could not apply them satisfactorily. If thin enough too many coats were required, if thicker the stuff could not be sprayed. Lacquer is quickly applied and therefore far cheaper than paint as a finish.

Competition with leather has resulted from the discovery of these tough, water-proof lacquer films, colored as they may be with various pigments. Strong cloth is sprayed with coat after coat of the desired lacquer and finally run through heavy rolls embossed with designs copied from the hides of alligators, snakes, and other creatures. Even hat bands and ballroom slippers may owe their coolness to the more delicate artificial leathers. Modern life would not be the same were there no cellulose derivatives.

Important as these uses of cellulose and its derivatives are they are dwarfed in comparison with the use of cellulose fiber, properly meshed and matted, as paper. Without paper, learn-

Zellerbach Paper Co.

FIG. 51. Making crude paper, papyrus, in ancient Egypt.

ing would be limited to the few, libraries would resemble brick yards with a clay tablet of Babylonian form for each page of book or, with rolls of animal skins like the old sheepskin diplomas, remind the readers of a tannery. The Egyptian papyrus of pounded split reeds was scarcely a paper but the Chinese paper of 2000 years ago was actually prepared by shaking a wet sludge of pounded bark on a sieve. In this way fibers of cellulose were intermeshed and a strong mat formed.

PAPER HAND MADE SHEET BY SHEET
ITS PRODUCTION A SECRET ART

Bjarne Johnson

FIG. 52. Hand-made paper would be woefully inadequate for the printed pages of today.

After the water drained away, the wet mat was pressed, much as in the hand-making of special papers today. Again we are indebted to the Moors for the introduction of a great art into Europe, about the eighth century. The continuous paper-making machine, invented by Fourdrinier in France about 1799 revolutionized the art—and brought learning to the common people. And yet the operation of this marvelous machine does not differ in fundamental principles from the hand work of the ancient Chinese paper makers.

A modern machine can make paper, rolling along from wet pulp to finished product, 17 feet wide, at a speed of 1200 feet per minute.

The best paper is made from linen rags, cellulose just the same, but since there is a limit to rags of linen and cotton, wood pulp in enormous quantities must be supplied. Much chemical and mechanical treatment is required—as is also more wood than the United States has available.

Charles Herty taught the South how to make good paper from slash pine, thus founding a domestic industry and strengthening national independence.

Nylon fiber, displacing much natural silk from the market, has become a factor in international affairs. Already Japan is greatly restricting silk production. This fiber is a duPont contribution to our national independence.

Nylon is spun from a polyamide resin formed from a diamine by condensation and polymerization until the product has a sufficiently high molecular weight and exhibits a fiber form under proper conditions. This plastic may be prepared in fiber, ribbons, sheets or rods. For fiber purposes a molecular weight of about 7000 seems best.

Nylon fabric for parachutes, nylon window cords, transparent nylon fly screens, nylon bristles for the tooth brush, nylon fabric for non-slip covers of auto seats, and nylon tennis strings are actual accomplishments. And nylon stockings!

Vinyon fiber, spun to a thread finer than silk is a polyvinyl acetate resin or plastic. It finds use in hosiery, waterproof clothing, fireproof awnings, acid and base resistant nets and in shower curtains.

Rayon cord for military tires, replacing cotton cord, is now demanded by the Army in the amount of 150,000,000 pounds. But nylon cord is stronger.

XVIII

MAN AGAINST PYGMY

TIME WAS when fierce saurians, gigantic in size, ranged the earth, defying all comers. They perished, however, through inability to adapt themselves to changing conditions. Then came man, surviving mastodon and saber-tooth tiger, dominant now over lion, tiger and elephant.

FIG. 53. Old triceratops weighed a few tons but our insect enemies are more terrible.

Man has proved to be more than a match for the giants among animals but will he conquer his pygmy enemies, the Insects?

No less an authority than L. O. Howard, former chief of the U. S. Bureau of Entomology, made this statement:

"If human beings are to continue to exist, they must first gain mastery over insects. Life may develop into a struggle between man and insects. . . . Insects in this country continually nullify the labor of one million men. Insects are better equipped to occupy the earth than humans, having been on the earth for 50,000,000 years, while the human race is but 500,000 years old."

Some great cataclysm of nature may wipe us out but what is a cataclysm to the million different species of insects? They have survived the worst and may perhaps be the last living creatures on earth. Their pygmy size and swift movements give them great powers of concealment while their enormous multiplications in spite of ravages by foes give them survival power by the sheer determinism of mathematics. Nor do they scorn to use Nature's tricks of protective coloration and shape. Finally, they wear their bones on the outside, unlike the vertebrates.

FIG. 54. The chemist enters the lists against insect enemies of mankind.

In this battle to the death the insects of earth eat our food, our clothing, our houses and, if that is not enough, they carry devastating diseases into our front-line trenches. Fernold estimates the annual losses due to insects in the United States alone as fully four billion dollars.

Field crops $1,667,200,000
Animals and their products 864,000,000
Loss by human disease and death 700,000,000
Forests, forest products and materials in storage ... 600,000,000
Farm wood lots 200,000,000

Added to this appalling total is the fruit loss and the $300,000,000 damage by clothes moths and the $100,000,000 spent for fly screens.

W. C. Allee of the University of Chicago does not minimize the seriousness of the conflict as he makes clear in "The Evolution of the Invertebrate."

"By most objective evidence, size of individual excepted, the insects of the arthropod series, rather than the mammals of the chordate series, are dominant on the earth today. They are most numerous in species and individuals—they are widespread. They practically control the great tropical region, the most fertile of the globe; only in rare instances, as in the eradication of mosquitoes from the Panama Canal Zone, has man been able to hold them sufficiently in check to go about  his work unharmed. In the less productive temperate regions, man is continually alert to circumvent the insects that carry disease to him and threaten to ruin his crops, to destroy his food supply. In time this may become the age of man, the most highly developed mentally of the vertebrates, but at present he is only beginning to dispute the ascendancy of his rivals, the highly specialized insects."

As disease carriers insects may well strike fear to our hearts. An insignificant flea carries the bubonic plague from infected rats and other rodents to human beings. As the Black Death, this disease once wiped out half the population of Europe and even now it is only by eternal vigilance that it is kept out of such great ports as San Francisco and New Orleans.

Another murderer is the mosquito, stabbing with a stiletto poisoned with the germs of yellow fever or malaria. The decline in vigor of the magnificent race of ancient Greeks was said to be due in part to imported malaria, debilitating the strongest. The mercenaries of Sulla and Marius carried malaria into the south of Italy to be spread by mosquitoes, depopulating the fertile Campagna near Rome and draining the strength from legions hard pressed by barbarians from the North. Nor is the story of malaria mere ancient history. There were 2,000,000 cases of malaria in Italy during 1900 and probably 1,500,000 in our own country.

The mosquito legions of Panama, equipped with yellow fever and malaria, defeated the French effort to dig an Isthmian Canal and it was only after a successful onslaught on these pygmies that the United States engineers were able to construct this wonder of the world. Within a lifetime outbreaks of yellow fever in our own South paralyzed commerce

and caused incredible hardship to the poor. Not so long ago
there were 3,000,000 deaths from malaria during a single
year in the British Empire with a greater toll in other regions
of the tropics. Now, thanks to the science of tropical medicine
there are only 500,000 malarial deaths yearly in the Empire.
However the tsetse fly, nocturnal carrier of the dreaded sleeping sickness, still makes life very hazardous for man and beast
in large areas of tropical Africa. New medicines have put

FIG. 55. The cotton boll weevil is insignificant in actual size yet every year he
ruins cotton worth hundreds of millions of dollars.

powerful weapons in the hands of the soldiers of science but
the battle against the tsetse fly still rages.

   Nearer home the common house fly carries typhoid fever
but, thanks to fly poisons, to screens, and to great care of our
supplies of water and milk, we have practically won that war.

   It is one of the ironies of science that improved means of
communication, our very internationalism, have brought to
our shores the voracious insects that lay a burdensome tax
upon every field, forest, and orchard. Airplanes crossing our
borders must now be searched for midget enemies. The air
lanes are dangerous in more ways than one. The Hessian
wheat fly, brought over with horse feed by the Hessian soldiers during the American Revolution, cost us millions before
we learned how to circumvent it. Of course the coddling moth
of Europe put worms in colonial apples. The gypsy moth, imported by accident in 1869 is winning, in spite of a few million
dollars spent every year in the fight.

   The most costly invader, perhaps, has been the cotton boll

weevil, carried across the border from Mexico in 1894. It eats the heart out of the tender young cotton boll—and out of the Southern farmer as well, with an annual loss of hundreds of millions of dollars. The corn borer is a recent comer to our shores and a most unwelcome one, adding to the burden already weighing too heavily on the farmer. The elm-leaf beetle, the Japanese beetle, the grasshopper, give us no respite in the struggle.

The locust plagues of Egypt, mentioned in the Bible, recur from time to time. Some twenty years ago they caused great losses in North Africa, East Africa and Central America. One swarm seen in Rhodesia was 60 miles long, 15 miles wide and 200 feet deep. The American version, the long-flying Western grasshopper, swept down upon the fields of South Dakota and Nebraska and ate every green crop. It was worse from 1873 to 1876, when swarms like dense black clouds impoverished whole states, west of the Mississippi.

Are we defenseless against these and other insect enemies? No, in spite of the fact that the menace has grown worse in the last ten years. The world is aroused and is bringing to bear its heavy artillery of chemical poisons, of parasites or other insect enemies of the dangerous insects, of quarantine, of improved crop practises, and of the development of resistant strains of plants.

The chemist is necessary, especially in acute emergencies of the battle. He contributes to the United States nearly 75,-000,000 pounds yearly of calcium arsenate, lead arsenate and Paris green as ammunition, not to mention oil for mosquito pools, hydrocyanic acid, HCN, for the citrus groves of California, lime-sulfur spray for orchards, Bordeaux mixture for garden and orchard, carbon disulfide and formaldehyde for treatment of seed grain, paradichlorbenzene for peach tree borers, DDT, and other chemical weapons.

Here is a most promising field for research of the utmost

service to humanity. Since some of these arsenical dusts or sprays injure the soil and make us think at least twice of their possible traces on unwashed fruits it is most important that we discover new compounds that are toxic to insects and safe for animals. Just now it seems that the silicofluorides, by-products in the preparation of superphosphate fertilizer from phosphate rock, may come near this requirement. Still more desirable is a white crystalline compound, called **rotenone**, obtained from a Brazilian plant. It is thirty times as toxic as nicotine to aphids, as unwelcome as lead arsenate to cater-

pillars, and yet has safely been fed to farm animals. Problem —to cultivate that Brazilian plant or to synthesize rotenone cheaply in the laboratory. Since its chemical structure has recently been determined there is hope that a light-resistant derivative may be synthesized for sunlight injures rotenone.

In 1935 our Department of Agriculture set a limit to tolerance for lead on apples and other sprayed foods, thus encouraging research on harmless but effective sprays.

Arsenic	0.010 grain per lb.	(1.4 parts per million)
Lead	0.018 " " "	(2.5 " " ")
Fluorine	0.010 " " "	(1.4 " " ")

Common pyrethrum plants yield two chemicals, deadly to many insects and only slightly toxic if at all to higher animals, now the base of most fly sprays or dusts. We import millions of pounds of pyrethrum flowers every year and are glad to get them.

Great areas of the South and Southwest were unsuitable

for cattle raising, because of the cattle tick, until a "dip" was prepared containing sodium arsenite, sodium cresylate (from coal tar) and soap. Australia has had a similar experience.

Dusting of cotton fields with calcium arsenate by machines and by airplanes, power-spraying of orchards, dusting mosquito swamps with Paris green by airplanes, pine forests with arsenicals from above or even with arsenical smoke candles and torches from below have become standard strategy on

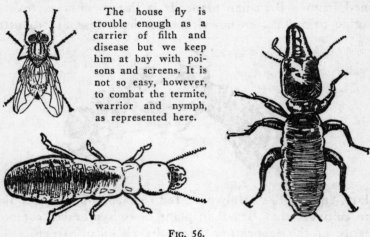

The house fly is trouble enough as a carrier of filth and disease but we keep him at bay with poisons and screens. It is not so easy, however, to combat the termite, warrior and nymph, as represented here.

Fig. 56.

the part of man. But some insects are tough—one of them even eats the protective lead sheath from electric cables.

Is it any wonder that our government declares an embargo on importation of a great list of plants, however desirable they may be? Too many costly immigrants of the insect race have been smuggled in that way.

The last foe to be listed here, and the one you probably know least about, is the termite, wrongly called the white ant. These persistent little wood eaters threaten every home built of wood—have already riddled sills, studding, joists, of houses in many states. The worst of it is that their presence in the interior of the wood may be quite unsuspected although the timber may be ready to collapse.

Supposed to be a tropical menace, distant and not dangerous to us, the wood termite is now widely scattered throughout the United States, ruining handsome homes in the vicinity of Washington and Indianapolis. Already they cost us $75,000,000 yearly and this bill may be multiplied several times before many years have passed.

The Capitol building in Washington has been attacked while government bonds in the Bureau of Engraving and Printing were eaten. Evidently termites insist on fresh bonds. They seem to desire a college experience also for they ate beams and books in one university in New York City. Sixty American corporations have become so alarmed that they joined in coöperative research against these insect enemies.

Termites are easily distinguished from winged ants by their very thick waists, in contrast to the extremely thin waists of the ants.

The subterranean termite—*reticulotermes,* to be exact—loves wood, darkness, and moisture. He enters wooden supports where they touch the moist earth (bad building on your part!) and stays out of sight in the heart of the wood. If you have wisely kept wood from coming in contact with the ground the termites may build little mud galleries up the face of the concrete foundation until they reach the coveted cellulose. Most termites need access to the moisture of the soil. Defeat their purpose, if you see such a structure—keep cutting off their lines of supply and they will die from dryness, says Dr. T. E. Snyder. But better yet protect your house in

the building. Have sills and other heavy timbers of the framework pressure-treated with coal tar creosote or with zinc chloride. There is practically no other effective preventative. Zinc chloride is washed out by rain so only interior timbers can be impregnated. Creosote has a slight odor and so needs to be covered with a coat or two of the best of the aluminum paints now being developed. Recently there has been prepared a most effective creosote distillate that is almost colorless and odorless.

There is little hope once termites get well started in an unprotected house for mere surface painting with creosote is ineffective. Treatment in pressure cylinders is required to secure good penetration.

Termites are effective because they are socially organized like the bee and the ant, with queen and males, sterile workers,

Fig. 57. The termite strikes terror to the heart of the staunchest wooden house.

young "nymphs" to be trained as desired for any career, and heavy-headed soldiers to protect against their arch-enemies the ants.

Insects are not wholly bad, for some friendly ones prey on the vicious ones. Then we owe much to the silkworm and to the bee.

References

"Prevention of Damage by Termites," *Farmers' Bulletin,* 1472, U. S. Dept. of Agriculture, 1926.

"How to Prevent Termite Damage to Buildings," *Engineering News-Record,* Vol. 100, 274-276, 1928.

"Termites and Termite Damage," U. of Cal. *Circular* 318 (1930).

"Termites and Termite Control," C. A. Kofoid and associates, Univ. of Cal. Press, 1934.

"Our Enemy the Termite," T. E. Snyder (U. S. Dept. Agr.), Comstock Pub. Co., Ithaca, N. Y., 1936.

XIX

FUELS AND SMOKE

WHEN THE world had one third its present population about two centuries ago, wood was the all-important fuel but wood no longer suffices. Even in the time of Elizabeth I England's forests were cut down and coal-mining extended. Until recently Abyssinia's capital had to be moved whenever firewood in the vicinity was exhausted.

Today the great fuel sources are coal, petroleum, natural gas, and their derivatives. Tomorrow there may be added sun mirrors operating solar engines or electric generators. The enormous amount of heat given off by the disintegration of radium tempts us to speculate on the release of the almost incalculably great energy of the atom. Atomic power is now a reality, not just a dream. If worse comes to worst, we may look to the farm as a source of power since "four tons of sugar, a moderate yield from one acre, yields 520 gallons of alcohol, enough to support two small automobiles traveling 8000 miles yearly."

The struggle for supremacy between the various sources of energy has been disturbing to business and to international relations, yet in the end the world profits. Coal has not gained in thirty years while fuel oil, natural gas and water power have made astonishing progress. Thirty years ago the mechanical power of the United States was divided among coal, 75 per cent, oil, 14 per cent, and natural gas, 4 per cent; the remainder from water power. The position of coal is worse now, only 50 per cent of the total for the world, natural gas and petroleum have taken much higher rank in the United States, and atomic power is a great threat. Greater efficiency in utilizing coal has cut down tonnage so much that the New York Trust Company estimates that the same energy can be produced today with 75 per cent as much coal as was required twenty years ago.

It is estimated that in 1956 energy sources in the United States compared as follows: coal, 29 per cent; petroleum, 42 per cent; natural gas, 25 per cent; water power, 4 per cent.

The white-maned horses leaping over the edge of a Niagara are racing against the black-maned horses released from coal mines. Put your money on the black.

Natural gas in the last few years has taken on new life and gives promise of a far greater future. The knowledge that it will burn is not new, for the "eternal fires" of the Parsee fire worshipers of 2500 years ago were merely flames of natural gas escaping from crevices in the rocks of oil regions. But the first gas well was drilled in 1821 near Fredonia, N. Y., where, three years later, Lafayette was astonished by gas light in his room. Fifty years later the real industry began in Pennsylvania and the last twenty years have seen unprecedented growth. Vast new supplies in Texas, California, and other states, with new methods of making high-pressure pipe lines, account for the recent change. Great pipe lines now carry natural gas from Texas and the adjoining states to New York, Chicago, California and other areas. And so there is new gas (we almost wrote "blood") in the metallic veins of an industry supposed to be dying of anemia some thirty years ago. While Chicago enjoys the convenience and cleanliness of a stream of 500,000,000 cubic feet daily the whole country burns 10,000 billion cubic feet annually.

Perhaps you have noticed that natural gas seems to be associated with petroleum pools. Naturally enough, for it is really the most volatile portion of petroleum. The greater part of this gas is methane, CH_4, and the remainder largely ethane, C_2H_6. Liquid petroleum is a mixture of many similar "hydrocarbons" or compounds of hydrogen and carbon, made up of heavier and less volatile molecules. Note the "structural formulas" of

$$\text{Methane } H - \overset{\displaystyle H}{\underset{\displaystyle H}{\overset{|}{\underset{|}{C}}}} - H \text{ and } H - \overset{\displaystyle H}{\underset{\displaystyle H}{\overset{|}{\underset{|}{C}}}} - \overset{\displaystyle H}{\underset{\displaystyle H}{\overset{|}{\underset{|}{C}}}} - H \text{ ethane.}$$

Those lines between atoms of carbon and hydrogen are conveniences in representing the attractions or valences (of electrical origin) that hold atoms together in the molecule, four for every carbon. It is this "tetravalence" of carbon that makes possible the bewildering multitude, perhaps 500,000, of carbon compounds. The heptane of very "high test" gasoline is C_7H_{16}, in agreement with the relation shown by the dozens of hydrocarbons found in petroleum. Note how C_nH_{2n+2} as a general formula fits CH_4, C_2H_6, C_3H_8, and all the rest. There are other series of hydrocarbons known, each with its own series relation convincing us of the existence of a magnificent order.

Methane is the simplest hydrocarbon possible and from it and ethane, by substituting chlorine or other active elements for one or more of the hydrogen atoms and otherwise manipulating the products, heavier hydrocarbons or their derivatives may be built. This is the art of the organic chemist. Long chains like:

$$H - \overset{\displaystyle H}{\underset{\displaystyle H}{\overset{|}{\underset{|}{C}}}} - \overset{\displaystyle H}{\underset{\displaystyle H}{\overset{|}{\underset{|}{C}}}} - \overset{\displaystyle H}{\underset{\displaystyle H}{\overset{|}{\underset{|}{C}}}} - \overset{\displaystyle H}{\underset{\displaystyle H}{\overset{|}{\underset{|}{C}}}} - \overset{\displaystyle H}{\underset{\displaystyle H}{\overset{|}{\underset{|}{C}}}} - \overset{\displaystyle H}{\underset{\displaystyle H}{\overset{|}{\underset{|}{C}}}} - \overset{\displaystyle H}{\underset{\displaystyle H}{\overset{|}{\underset{|}{C}}}} - H, \text{ heptane,}$$

are possible in carbon chemistry but any attempt to build up similar compounds with tetravalent silicon of quartz only results in breaking the backbone of all but the shortest chains.

Carbon chemistry is unique, without a rival.

Petroleum is the real "liquid gold" of commerce, driving much of our merchant marine and our navy, all of the world's 60,000,000 motor cars and its airplanes, and many locomotives; furnishing light to rural homes and power for farm machinery; heating a rapidly increasing number of houses and office buildings; and lubricating nearly all of the machines in an age of machines.

Yet before Drake's venture near Oil City, Pennsylvania, in 1859, there never had been a well drilled with the sole purpose of getting petroleum. Salt wells had been ruined by oil as early as 1829 and the Seneca Indians had soaked up oil films on water pools with blankets, later to be squeezed out as "medicine."

It is no longer an "infant industry" but a giant with many billions invested in the United States and, in prosperous years, an annual flow of nearly 2,750,000,000 barrels, nearly half of the world production. Venezuela, Iraq, with other Middle East areas, and Russia have other important fields. Occasional overproduction is a temporary phase; conservation of such irreplaceable resources must come.

The refining of petroleum is largely a series of distillation steps, at first by flame and later by steam. It seems difficult to believe that as late as 1906 the primary product was kerosene for lamps. Now the primary product is gasoline as motor fuel, although the lubricants are valuable and the fuel oil in great demand. The production of the principal products today is approximately as follows:

Gasoline (and naphtha)	42.0	per cent of the crude oil
Kerosene	5.3	" " " " " "
Fuel oil (and gas oil)	40.2	" " " " " "
Lubricants	3.7	" " " " " "

Just before World War I Burton introduced the "cracking" of the heavier and less salable molecules of the higher-boiling fractions to yield the smaller molecules making up gasoline (C_6H_{14}, C_7H_{16}, and C_8H_{18}) and thus nearly doubled the production of gasoline. This making two blades of grass grow where one grew before lowered the price of gasoline, helped the average citizen. Heating at 375° C. under 100 pounds pressure caused the cracking or splitting of molecules but of course great improvements have followed the original Burton process. In some plants steel towers built like cannon withstand pressures of 1000 pounds or much more, at temperatures of 1000° F. In ordinary years this country requires 30,000,000,000 gallons of gasoline yet few people realize that more than one tenth of this total is condensed from natural gas and used in blends to yield the best "hightest" gasoline.

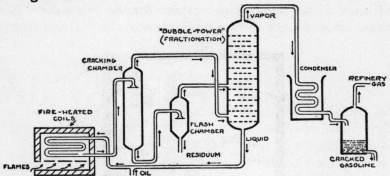

FIG. 58. Petroleum cracking has more than doubled the yield of gasoline possible by the old distillation methods.

We now force hydrogen under great pressure to unite with cracked molecules; we force small molecules to polymerize (build up larger aggregates from smaller units) to yield high octane number gasoline; and we convert straight chain molecules into branched chain molecules of high antiknock value or into the ring compounds such as toluene, hitherto obtained from coal distillation.

The "bottled gas" now sold as a convenient gaseous fuel for isolated homes or small towns, is the butane, C_4H_{10}, byproduct of oil refining or of extraction of gasoline from natural gas. Not volatile enough for gas mains and too volatile for motor fuel it is compressed to liquid form in steel cylinders and widely distributed. This and the still more volatile propane, C_3H_8, are sold to the extent of about four billion gallons annually, and the market is growing. Thirty years ago only one million gallons were sold.

When oil is exhausted, oil shales of Colorado, Indiana and other sections will be distilled, chemically converted into petroleum, one barrel from one ton of shale. With each

square mile of the 1500 in the Colorado area alone capable of
yielding 24,000,000 barrels of oil there is good prospect that
the huge motor industry will continue. And there are other
resources in sight.

In spite of competition coal is still the backbone of power.
Of the 1,500,000,000 tons consumed by the world every busy
year this country produces and uses one third. Some of it is

Phila. and Reading Coal Co.

FIG. 59. Put your chimney in a test tube. Analysis of the flue gases may save fuel.

burned as dust, blown into the combustion chamber with a
stream of air, and now we hear of the invention of a dust explosion engine supposed to be very economical.

The recent growth in size of boilers due to use of powdered coal burners—and oil spray burners—is amazing. In
1924, a 3000 horse power boiler in Pittsburgh was considered
the marvel of the country. A later giant was a New York
Edison boiler evaporating 1,000,000 pounds of steam every
hour, furnishing 35,000 horse power. The dedication luncheon
was served in this boiler to 97 guests who, as they looked
up to the arching forests of tubes, almost imagined they were
seated in a Gothic cathedral.

A modern plant of two boilers, using mercury vapor instead of steam, furnishes 12,000 horse power each. There are advantages—and the disadvantages that 125 tons of this metal at over $1.00 per pound are required for each boiler. If many such installations are ordered the world's mercury production of 5000 tons yearly must be increased.

It will be centuries before our coal supplies are exhausted and by that time we can use the enormous beds of lignite or

FIG. 60. Gas tanks fill the eye when black, and blend with the sky when coated with aluminum paint.

brown coal found in South Dakota and elsewhere. There is always a way out.

Coke, essential to the steel industry, must be made by heating bituminous coal without access of air in "coke ovens." Before World War I Germany caught and used all the gaseous products from coke ovens—and we did not. Our reform is complete for the modern by-product coke oven is almost universally used.

The coal gas obtained is an excellent fuel much used in cities; the ammonia so separated in the United States in 1956 made 2,000,000 tons of ammonium sulfate as fertilizer for our farms; the coal tar condensed from this distillation of "soft" coal yielded many chemicals from which were made dyes, medicines, antiseptics, explosives, wood preservatives; the benzene (benzol) volatilized became the starting point for intricate chemical processes—and served as an excellent anti-knock fuel; and the pitch left behind surfaced our roads.

Not until 1812 did Murdock introduce coal gas lighting of streets to London. Paris soon followed and Baltimore began to light its streets with coal gas in 1816.

A net ton of coking-coal yields about 1440 pounds of coke, or 72 per cent by weight, together with 9 gallons of tar, 22 pounds of sulfate of ammonia, 2½ gallons of crude benzol, and 10,000 cubic feet of gas. Of the latter, about half is needed for heating the ovens so that the balance, 5000 feet, is available for power.

Gaseous fuels are always in great demand—natural gas, coal gas from coke ovens, water gas from coke and steam ($H_2 + CO$) and cheap producer gas made by blowing air and steam up through layers of coal five or six feet deep. Properly burned they are all smokeless.

Smoke palls over cities once brought a reassuring feeling of prosperity to the observer. Now smoke is recognized as an enemy to beauty, health, and the lasting qualities of fabrics and stone buildings. Corrosion of certain building stones, concrete and iron by the sulfuric acid in smoke is serious. Furthermore the tarry matter in smoke coats the droplets of moisture in fogs and makes them last longer. London and Pittsburgh are tired of being cited as the world's dirtiest cities nor will Chicago care to believe that 460 tons of soot and dust fall on its every square mile each year. Queen Elizabeth I was so disgusted with smoke that she refused to let her subjects burn coal in London during a session of Parliament and one King Edward hanged a man for this offense.

Pittsburgh deserves great credit for an aggressive clean-air campaign that cut her smoke deposit to a fraction of its former value. Manufacturers coöperated splendidly, putting in automatic stokers and using all reasonable precautions, yet household smoke continued.

Automatic stokers feed fuel to the fire from the bottom

so that there is always flame on the surface to ignite gaseous products distilled from a fresh charge of coal. Consequently there is little or no smoke resulting. The recent invention of a household size of such stokers will go far towards restoring our somewhat smudged civic pride. The rapidly growing use of oil spray burners is another forward step in smoke prevention.

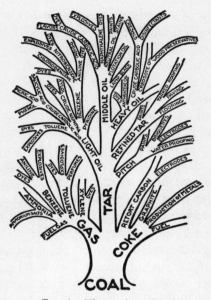

FIG. 61. The coal tar tree.

Yet there is one industry that thrives on good black smoke—the making of gas black by burning natural gas with insufficient air. The smoky flame resulting supplies us with one billion pounds of gas black each year in the United States to be used in printers' ink, carbon papers and as a strengthener of automobile tires. We pay well from our natural resources for this black for it takes 700,000,000,000 cubic feet of natural gas to meet our yearly demands for gas black. The inferior lampblack made from smoky flames of burning tars is not an adequate substitute—the particles are too large.

XX

CHEMISTRY AND THE
MOTOR CAR

THE RESOURCES of chemistry have been heavily drawn upon to make the modern motor car and to satisfy its ravenous appetite for fuel, lubricants and decoration.

The traditional methods of oil refining have been radically changed to meet this demand for gasoline to supply our 40,000,000 automobiles (a great fraction of the world's 60,000,000) and for lubricants to stand the pace. Thus stimulated, the petroleum industry enters the chemical markets in order to dispose of by-products and new synthetic products.

Poverty of natural resources forced Germany to devise processes to convert her abundant coal into gasoline. Rubber production in the East Indies was forced to expand manyfold with great improvement in quality. Chemical resourcefulness increased the life of tires from 8000 miles in 1920 to 30,000 miles in 1956. Alloy steels to meet the exacting demands of oil refiner and of car manufacturer had to be invented. In fact if your car were made of ordinary steel it would have the weight of a lumbering old truck in order to provide the strength and vibration resistance now demanded. Safety glass of high quality and low cost had to be produced by the square mile. Nitrocellulose lacquers, consuming quantities of cellulose, nitric acid, and acetic acid, and new solvents, were needed. The storage battery industry was completely inadequate and was forced to phenomenal growth. Concrete roads spun their lengths as motor cars increased in numbers. That "Chemistry made the motor car" is a claim with considerable foundation.

The auto industry is the largest buyer of steel, rubber, plate glass, nickel, lead, leather, malleable iron, and a heavy buyer of aluminum, copper, tin and lumber.

"Duco" puts money in the pocket of every car owner and

gives him better service at that. Forty years ago lacquer sprays were limited to 5 per cent content of cellulose nitrate. This was later increased to 22 per cent, thanks to the low-viscosity type of cellulose nitrate and to some special treatment. Heavier lacquer coating is thus secured with fewer sprayings. No longer do you pay for the delay and costly labor of applying many coats of paint.

The diesel engine, exploding heavy fuel oil by high compression instead of electric ignition, is both partner and rival of the automobile. It has a present in power plants, in driving certain marine craft and most of our trains as well as highly odorous motor trucks. War research brought its weight far below the previous ratio of 30 pounds per horse power.

FIG. 62. The automobile has exerted a profound influence on our civilization.

The science of safety for auto travel is no longer mechanical and psychological—it is chemical as well. Careful study indicates that fully seven per cent of motor cars when in operation contain dangerous amounts of carbon monoxide. Dangerous because the slowing down of the driver's mental process by this insidious poison is a frequent cause of accidents. Automobile exhaust gas often contains seven per cent of carbon monoxide.

The stupendous growth of the motor industry has had a far-reaching influence on chemical industry. For example great nations with plenty of coal but no petroleum are driven to desperate scientific research in order to maintain employment at home and to secure a greater degree of independence in war. Many years ago Bergius in Germany hydrogenated lignite coal, powdered and mixed with heavy oil, under high temperatures and pressures. Gasoline, diesel oil, fuel oil and coke resulted. Germany supported this industry as a way to economic and military independence although for some years the cost was much greater than for similar products prepared from imported petroleum. Their annual production was probably about 200,000 tons of gasoline, far greater now.

It is a matter of importance that England has built a Bergius plant, beginning operation late in 1935, with a capacity of 150,000 tons (not gallons) of gasoline annually. Four tons of coal yield one ton of gasoline. Hydrogenation takes place in a strong steel autoclave at 450° C. under a pressure of 250 atmospheres. Government favor in some form is probably necessary for the success of this industry in both countries.

Who would have dreamed that the motor car would force extraction of bromine on a large scale from the ocean, even from the Dead Sea? Yet the demand for anti-knock fuel with resulting greater power has united ethylene gas, by-product of petroleum cracking, and the bromine extracted from salt brines so that "ethyl gas" became possible.

Ethylene bromide, $C_2H_4Br_2$, is a simple addition product formed by contact of ethylene with bromine water. It is used with tetra ethyl lead, $Pb\ (C_2H_5)_4$, in "ethyl gas" to convert the lead after explosion into lead bromide, less harmful to ignition points, and people.

Without the revolutionary improvements in petroleum refining of the past twenty years, there would not be half enough gasoline for our needs. Demand forced these improvements. As a secondary result four billion gallons of liquefied refinery gas were used last year for cooking in isolated homes, for municipal gas systems in smaller towns, and for bus fuel. Other unsaturated gases from the refinery were treated with sulfuric acid and water to yield alcohols from which solvents for lacquers are made. It is possible to make common grain alcohol in this way, a disturbing thought to farmers expecting to make more alcohol from corn for addition to motor fuel. Petroleum refineries are now producing toluene, glycerine, rubber and many other chemicals, including ethyl alcohol.

Petroleum chemistry is motor car chemistry.

XXI

BORN TO THE PURPLE

TWO THOUSAND years ago royalty and the wealthiest nobility were "born to the purple" for only they could afford to pay $600 a pound for cotton cloth dyed with the precious secretion of *murex,* a tiny shellfish of the Eastern Mediterranean. The distinction associated with inherited wealth really belonged to the modest *murex* which had brains enough to secrete di-brom indigo.

Since shellfish are notoriously silent the secret of the composition of the purple dye was kept through the ages until Friedlander in 1909 analyzed this "Tyrian purple," which had once brought wealth to the merchants of ancient Tyre, and found it to be identical with a synthetic derivative of indigo prepared five years earlier and discarded as inferior. How are the mighty fallen! The most regal dye of those bygone days of fabulous Oriental magnificence now rejected as not good enough for the pampered taste of shop girls!

It is the fashion now to sigh for the days of the "vegetable dyes" and to refer to modern "coal tar dyes" as glaring and fugitive. As a matter of fact these vegetable dyes were few in number and very unexciting in beauty—only logwood black and fustian yellow surviving the competition. Now, thanks to coal tar chemistry, a thousand dyes of every conceivable hue are offered for your capricious taste and, if you insist, four thousand more could be marketed. In the United States over $30,000,000 annually are spent in dye research in order that milady may be gowned more beautifully than the Queen of Sheba.

And it is all comparatively recent, since 1856, although in a sense coal tar chemistry properly began in 1825 with Faraday's isolation of benzene, C_6H_6, from coal gas. A year later aniline, the parent of half the dyes now made, was prepared by a method now obsolete. It ought to have been made from benzene in the first place, as it now is, but history is not always logical.

No further progress towards a dye industry was made until 1856 when William Perkin, an English lad of seventeen or eighteen, studying with the great German chemist Hofmann, in London, decided to synthesize quinine. He was

Parke Davis Co.

FIG. 63. The boy who found rainbows in coal tar.
William Perkin, youthful dreamer, makes the first aniline dye, mauve, in his father's attic (1856).

rather ambitious for his years and perhaps not very logical in his attempt to secure this natural product by oxidizing aniline with chromic acid. A black, tarry mess was his reward. In youthful disgust William washed out the tar with alcohol and obtained a purple solution, **mauve**, the first coal tar dye or aniline dye ever prepared. True to the traditions of his great teacher the young chemist repeated the experiment, improving on it by the use of a purer aniline. But it was no improvement for the beautiful purple failed to flash again. Persistent trials brought out the important fact that a trace of toluidine impurity in the aniline was necessary.

Perkin formed a company to exploit his dye and to make others, but England yawned. That yawn was to cost the Empire countless lives and untold treasure from 1914 to 1918. The aniline dye industry was promptly transferred to Germany and developed magnificently to such a point that in 1913 Germany made three-fourths of the world's dyes. The world supported in the fatherland a great force of highly trained chemists, able and ready in an emergency to make explosives and war gases; paid for factories and laboratories that could overnight be adapted to manufacture of war munitions.

This blind, fatuous dependence upon Germany for dyes, essential medicines, and related products turned the joke on us—if there could be any joke in those four tragic years. Certain allied uniforms and flags were not dyed as usual until some dyes were smuggled out of Germany. The production and sale of a billion dollars' worth of cloth in Great Britain was seriously hampered for lack of dyes. Nor were we any better off in this country. The dye industry, we soon learned, is a "key" industry, important beyond any cash value of its products. We will never be caught again in the same trap. In 1956 our country made 160,000,000 pounds of dyes—and exported some.

But to come back to our story. "Turkey red" had long been a favorite color, a vegetable color if that interests you. Great areas of France were devoted to the growing of madder root which contained the dye. Then in 1868 Graebe and Liebermann in Germany determined the structure of the red molecule and proceeded to synthesize it from the anthracene found in coal tar. Perkin (later to be known as Sir William) independently made the same discovery but was just one day late in reaching the patent office. He lost a great prize thereby, for in a short time Germany was selling $8,000,000 worth of synthetic alizarin annually. The product was actually better than the extract of the madder root, so those French fields were released for food production.

A typical triumph of chemical science was the successful

production of synthetic indigo. Typical, too, of Teutonic patience and a lesson to some American manufacturers who expect miracles overnight from their research staff. The great Badische company spent twenty years of effort and $5,000,-000 of treasure before success rewarded them. From naphthalene (common moth ball stuff) to indigo, sounds simple and direct but there were many steps and many troubles. The prize was great for the natural product of the indigo plant grown in the rich fields of India sold yearly to the value of $20,000,000. In 1913 India produced practically none—and was free to raise food on those fertile acres. A century ago this dye, more used than any other then as now, cost $4.00 a pound. Today it can be had at thirty cents a pound in car lots and of a purity and quality unknown to the original vegetable product.

•   •   •

Organic, or carbon chemistry dealing with its 275,000 compounds is distinguished by two very great classes, the petroleum series and the coal tar series or, more sharply, derivatives of the methane, CH_4, of natural gas and derivatives of benzene, C_6H_6, distilled from soft coal.

You may recall how the atoms of carbon and hydrogen are linked together in methane, ethane, and the similar hydrocarbons of the series found mixed in petroleum.

$$H-\overset{\displaystyle H}{\underset{\displaystyle H}{\overset{|}{\underset{|}{C}}}}-H \; , \; H-\overset{\displaystyle H}{\underset{\displaystyle H}{\overset{|}{\underset{|}{C}}}}-\overset{\displaystyle H}{\underset{\displaystyle H}{\overset{|}{\underset{|}{C}}}}-H \; \text{ and } \; H-\overset{\displaystyle H}{\underset{\displaystyle H}{\overset{|}{\underset{|}{C}}}}-\overset{\displaystyle H}{\underset{\displaystyle H}{\overset{|}{\underset{|}{C}}}}-\overset{\displaystyle H}{\underset{\displaystyle H}{\overset{|}{\underset{|}{C}}}}-\overset{\displaystyle H}{\underset{\displaystyle H}{\overset{|}{\underset{|}{C}}}}-\overset{\displaystyle H}{\underset{\displaystyle H}{\overset{|}{\underset{|}{C}}}}-\overset{\displaystyle H}{\underset{\displaystyle H}{\overset{|}{\underset{|}{C}}}}-H,$$

The third member above is hexane, C_6H_{14}, just a little too volatile for a good gasoline. Now the benzene, C_6H_6, discovered by Faraday in coal gas and by Hofmann in coal tar, failed to act chemically as if its carbons were tied together in a "chain" like the hexane. Chemists were puzzled, among them Kekulé who carried the problem on his mind even in dreams. While dozing by the fire one evening he fancied that he saw chains of molecules dancing and rolling in space. Suddenly one snake-like chain swallowed its own tail and rolled around like the mythical hoop snake. Kekulé awoke with a start, seized pencil and paper, and set down diagrams or structural formulas suggested by the dream.

That Kekulé's dream was inspired by worry and not by wine, is evident from the results. He soon tested out thoroughly his idea that the six carbons of benzene (erroneously called "benzol" by the public) formed a six-membered ring, and rested his case with the jury of science. That was in 1858 and none has since successfully denied his theory.

Fortunately the way for benzene development had been prepared a few years earlier at a brilliant reception in the Tuilleries. To grace the occasion with a special touch, wax candles bleached by chlorine were used. The gay company, sobered by the presence of an irritating gas in the air, left early. Dumas, called in to explain the incident, recognized hydrochloric acid gas, HCl, and pointed out that chlorine atoms had replaced one or more hydrogen atoms in the wax molecules with formation of HCl released during burning. This substitution, easily understood when applied to methane,

$$H - \underset{\underset{H}{|}}{\overset{\overset{H}{|}}{C}} - H + Cl_2 \rightarrow H - \underset{\underset{H}{|}}{\overset{\overset{H}{|}}{C}} - Cl + HCl.$$

captured the fancy of chemists everywhere. They tried to substitute atoms, or even groups of atoms, in benzene—with magnificent success. Empires have tottered as a result. See what happens when nitric acid pries loose one hydrogen in exchange for its own nitro group, — NO_2, and what follows when hydrogen freshly released from an acid revenges itself on that nitro group, converting nitro-benzene, $C_6H_5NO_2$, into aniline, $C_6H_5NH_2$.

Benzene → Nitrobenzene → Aniline

It is this aniline, so sensitive to attack by many chemicals, that has been led to bloom into the rainbow of beauty of a thousand aniline dyes. The anthracene from which alizarin, the world's greatest red dye, is prepared has a molecule in which three benzene rings are bound side by side. In the process of making alizarin it is attacked by sulfuric acid which trades a sulfonic group, —SO_3H, for a single hydrogen; fused with caustic soda to force an exchange of an —ONa group for the —SO_3H group; and at the same time oxidized to obtain two oxygen atoms for two hydrogen atoms; and so on. Do not trouble to remember this but give a little credit to the dye chemist who must obviously have mastered the art of trading.

Now note how a chemist skilled in the art of dye manufacture can quickly be enlisted in the national defense. Granted that he knows how to nitrate benzene, why not nitrate toluene, also obtained from coal tar? It is done by nitric acid, with a forced exchange of three nitro groups for three hydrogen atoms—and T.N.T., trinitrotoluene, one of the mightiest high explosives known, results.

Benzene   Toluene   T.N.T.

"Carbolic acid," or phenol, is also obtained from coal tar but the French needs for ammonium picrate during World War I demanded twenty times our normal production of phenol. The additional millions of pounds were made from benzene by the attack of sulfuric acid and a fusion of the product with potassium hydroxide. Then this phenol was nitrated to yield yellow picric acid and neutralized with ammonia to form the powerful explosive, ammonium picrate, favored by French armies. Never mind the details but compare the structural formulas.

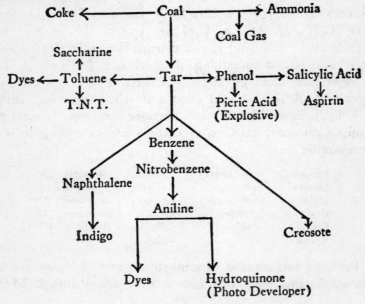

Now great quantities of phenol are made by chlorinating benzene and heating the product at high pressure with sodium hydroxide.

Evidently many things, some far more complicated than those above, come from coal tar. Look at the following rather abbreviated chart.

XXII

SUGARS AND SWEET-NESS

THE MODERN American tries to approximate "sweetness and light" for he eats 108 pounds of sugar every twelve months. To tell such a gastronomic authority that not all sweet things are sugars nor all sugars sweet is to court skepticism. However it is simply a matter of molecular structure and the sweet taste is merely incidental, only occasionally so at that.

Saccharine is 500 times as sweet, and perillaldehyde 2,000 times as sweet, as cane sugar yet in the inner arrangement of atoms they fail to qualify as sugars. You see the sugars share with cellulose and starch the honor of the name "carbohydrate," a name signifying that carbon is linked to exactly twice as many hydrogen atoms as oxygen atoms. If hydrogen and oxygen chose to break away from the carbohydrate molecule they would form water, H_2O. Look at $C_{12}H_{22}O_{11}$ cane sugar, $C_6H_{12}O_6$ glucose, $C_6H_{10}O_5$ starch. There isn't any water in rock candy, yet if you disrupt the molecules by heat, water escapes and something like carbon is left behind. You can remember that all these so-called sugars are carbohydrates and all have — OH groups attached to carbon atoms. That distinction will serve our purpose just now. It suits the chemist's purpose, also, to give them names ending in -ose. For example

Sucrose	(cane sugar)	$C_{12}H_{22}O_{11}$	sweetness	100
Lactose	(milk sugar)	$C_{12}H_{22}O_{11}$	sweetness	16
Maltose	(malt sugar)	$C_{12}H_{22}O_{11}$	sweetness	32
Dextrose	(glucose)	$C_6H_{12}O_6$	sweetness	74
Levulose	(fructose)	$C_6H_{12}O_6$	sweetness	173
Xylose		$C_6H_{12}O_6$		

Perhaps you wonder why maple sugar and honey are not included in this list? The fact is they are included. Maple sugar is nothing but cane sugar plus some delicious impurities contributed by the maple tree, while honey is a mixture of dextrose and levulose into which the bees' legs have stirred the well-flavored pollen of flowers. Differences in flavor and color of honey are credited to the various flowers visited by the bees, strong, dark honey coming from buckwheat bloom and pale yellow, mild nectar from clover blossoms, or orange flowers. No other sugar maker works as hard as the honey bee with its 10,000 flights for each pound of product, a total travel record of 40,000 miles.

You may fail to inquire why beet sugar is not mentioned, through fear of displaying your ignorance. If pure, as it usually is, beet sugar is identical with cane sugar—merits the name of sucrose.

Speaking of purity of product, isn't it amazing that we buy in the United States over seven million tons annually of this white, crystalline sucrose, practically 100 per cent pure, at the trifling cost of nine or ten cents per pound? We buy—but produce only one fifth of our needs, trusting largely to Cuba to fill our sugar bowl.

They say that "blood will tell" and they might as well add that the sweet juice of modern cane and beet will tell of an aristocracy of good breeding. Plant breeders, by guided selection, have given us a variety of cane containing juice of 16 per cent sugar strength, doubling the sugar content of more primitive cane. When sugar was first extracted from beets in 1747 by a German, the juice held only six per cent sugar but now the farmer considers his labor wasted if his beets fail to yield three times that much sugar. The richer the juice the less the labor and the lower the cost of the final product.

You may remember that the French Academy offered a prize for the discovery of a new process of making soda— and so had some share in the Le Blanc process. With the same aim, to make France independent of British naval interference with commerce, Napoleon offered a million francs for a practical process of extracting sugar from beets—and founded a great agricultural industry for France.

The war shortage of sugar brought home to all of us a vivid realization of the value and pleasure that sugar adds to the diet. In vain we tried to substitute malt sugar but appetite rebelled against the slight beery flavor. Today we could purify maltose if there was any financial profit in it.

In war times we were far from reluctant to pour "corn syrup" on the breakfast pancake but there was no pure, crystallized glucose to be had. Today we can produce such a sugar in unlimited quantities, and we do to the amount of over one billion pounds of this excellent corn sugar, dextrose, glucose, call it what you will. The police call it worse names, for they maintain that most of the supply is fermented into "bootleg" liquors, that glucose kings are no better than bootleg barons. Things came to such a pass in Cleveland that courts debated the rights of policemen to follow customers home with their glucose.

The conversion of corn starch (or any starch) into dextrose (glucose) is so simple that you will, possibly, permit insertion of the chemical equation appropriate at this point. Heated with water containing only 0.1 per cent hydrochloric acid, "hydrolysis" of the starch readily takes place, water adds on to the molecule. Of course the acid is finally neutralized by soda with no unpleasant taste resulting.

$$C_6H_{10}O_5 + H_2O \rightarrow C_6H_{12}O_6.$$
$$\text{Starch} \qquad\qquad \text{Glucose}$$

Unfortunately other reactions complicate the story and your "corn syrup" is a mixture of 20 per cent glucose, 45 per cent maltose, and 35 per cent gummy dextrin, all perfectly good foods.

For fear some pedantic chemist may tell you that there are sixteen possible sugars of the formula $C_6H_{12}O_6$, fourteen already discovered, we must hasten to save your sanity. A glance at the structural formula of one of the sixteen, glucose, reveals all the possibilities.

$$H - \overset{\overset{\displaystyle H}{|}}{C} - \overset{\overset{\displaystyle H}{|}}{C} - \overset{\overset{\displaystyle H}{|}}{C} - \overset{\overset{\displaystyle H}{|}}{C} - \overset{\overset{\displaystyle H}{|}}{C} - \overset{\overset{\displaystyle H}{|}}{C} = O \text{, glucose.}$$
$$\underset{OH}{|} \; \underset{OH}{|} \; \underset{OH}{|} \; \underset{OH}{|} \; \underset{OH}{|}$$

Imagine that you have rotated one of these carbon atoms with its upper and lower dependents until the H is below and the OH above. You then have a different sugar. You can play several variations on this theme although of course nobody believes the glucose molecule to be as flat as this sheet of paper. The research required to discover the molecular structure of this and the many other sugars was tremendously difficult, carried out by some of the greatest men in chemistry and in the end may seem to you as nothing better than academic gymnastics. But be careful! We can transform cellulose itself into sugars and we know that dextrose units make up the heavy molecule of cellulose. The more we learn about sugars the more we shall know about cellulose, the greatest crop on earth. Cellulose understood is cellulose tamed.

A twin of dextrose in the sense that left and right hands are twins, is levulose, a sugar that you may hear more of in future years. This right and left terminology refers to their rotation of the vibration plane of polarized light, a wonderful phenomenon but a bit technical for us at this stage of our education. Both dextrose and levulose have the same formula, $C_6H_{12}O_6$, but the atoms in the molecules are arranged differently. Curiously enough when you add a little lemon juice or vinegar or sour "cream of tartar" to cane sugar, as in making smooth fondant for chocolate creams, you split the heavy molecule into the twins. It is the acid that catalyzes, aids, this reaction with water, commonly termed "inversion" of sugar.

$$C_{12}H_{22}O_{11} + H_2O \rightarrow C_6H_{12}O_6 + C_6H_{12}O_6.$$
$$\text{Sucrose} \qquad\qquad \text{Dextrose} \quad \text{Levulose}$$

Quite parallel to the conversion of starch to dextrose is the conversion of inulin, a carbohydrate found in dahlia tubers and the Jerusalem artichoke (tuber variety), to levulose. Our

Department of Agriculture with fatherly kindness has selected the most prolific artichoke, developed a factory process for making pure levulose, and presented it to the public. The yield per acre is amazing, up to 14 tons of tubers, and with levulose ranking as nearly twice as sweet as cane sugar it would seem that something ought to be done about it.

Milk sugar, lactose, is extracted from skim milk to the extent of 5,000,000 pounds annually but many times this quantity could easily be produced if justified by demand. It has value as infants' food and in treatment of intestinal disorders but it does not taste very sweet. Now comes discovery of a form called beta lactose which tastes much sweeter (because more quickly dissolved) and so should be more popular in the diet.

If you crave some newer novelty among the sugars you might consider xylose, once sold for $100 the pound, and now cheaply prepared on an experimental scale from cottonseed hulls. It is novel, for this sugar has only five carbon atoms in the molecule instead of the usual six or twelve. Although sweet they say it does not digest. Still there may be uses for all the xylose to be made from our 1,500,000 tons of cottonseed hull bran.

The last sugar we care to list here is a poison. Chemists at Yale have extracted from the tuberculosis bacillus a very peculiar sugar, that, when injected into the human body, produced all the symptoms of tuberculosis. No, we shall make a better chapter ending than that. There are firms making a specialty of selling to bacteriologists several very rare sugars, each one the favorite food of some strain of bacteria. Consequently a bacillus may be recognized by the particular sugar it utilizes. The science of medicine has profited from this knowledge.

XXIII

FATS TO THE FRONT

FATS LOOM large in world affairs, in industry, even in the household, and deserve a broader consideration than the average citizen gives them. Of course in the life of the family they are recognized as essential to the balanced diet and as the basis of soap-making, perhaps as a factor in cosmetics.

But how many realize that a fat, linseed oil, is the liquid part of paint, that it made possible the Corots and Rembrandts that enrich life for those with artistic taste? You may doubt that art is always in evidence with every sample of linoleum, though the best of it really is beautiful. In any event there would be no such convenient and serviceable floor covering without fatty oils. The time may come when the tropics will produce liquid fats as fuels in competition with gasoline. Peanut oil made in the Tanganyika district of Africa has already been tried in the diesel engines of river steamboats. Egloff has "cracked" cottonseed oil at 900° F. and 150 pounds pressure to yield gasoline, diesel engine oil, gases, and coke. Peanut oil could be treated successfully in the same way.

It is of passing interest to learn that the peanut industry developed in Tanganyika by Germany once gave $20,000,000 annually to the British Empire. To develop further this theme of international interest in fats do you know that Germany, producing insufficient fat from farm animals, tried to introduce the Manchurian soy bean because of its 20 per cent fat content and failed, due to unfavorable soil and climate. Were she able to grow cotton, or corn, or peanuts, or olive trees her independence would be greater. She needs to import fats as food, as soap stock, and as the source of the glycerine to be converted into nitroglycerine and dynamite.

Now that you are demanding more than the mere name

of a product and have become chemically-minded you will doubtless be delighted to learn that a fat is a combination of glycerine with one or more "fatty acids" of high molecular weight. So glyceryl oleate accounts for the larger fraction of olive oil; glyceryl stearate, oleate, and palmitate for a good fraction of such solid fats as tallow and lard; while butter is a mixture of glyceryl butyrate and about fifteen other fats. By the way, rancidity in butter is due to the liberation of butyric acid, recognizable by its extremely unpleasant odor. Any fat may be split into glycerine (always glycerine) and the fatty acids, stearic, palmitic, oleic, linoleic, butyric, or any others of the dozens known.

In 1942 Argentina produced 500,000 tons of edible sunflower seed oil and sold one fourth of it to us. Kansas ought to earn its name as the "sunflower state." Almond oil, castor bean oil, peanut oil, corn oil, soy bean oil, coconut oil we all know, but have you heard of chaulmoogra oil, expressed from the seeds of a rather rare tree in the East Indies? In this fat lies a faint hope of a cure for leprosy, yet the medicine is almost too indigestible for endurance. Consequently chemists have split this fat, coupled its acids with other alcohols than glycerine and, in general, substituted things in the molecule in the hope that the good effects might be retained while the bad might be cast aside. A fair degree of success has rewarded such efforts, but the sulfones offer more promise.

Do you know that the bacteria of tuberculosis are richer in fat or wax than any other living thing—that they contain nearly 40 per cent? Chemists at Yale have grown cultures of tubercle bacilli on a factory basis, separated this fat or wax, injected it into animals and produced some of the disorders associated with the disease. It is quite different from all other fats, a trouble maker.

The variety of fats in nature continues to astonish us. "A few years ago J. G. Martin of Sturgeon Bay, Wisconsin, stepped on a cherry pit. The results were a grease spot on the floor and the birth of a new industry. Now Mr. Martin is making oil from a thousand tons of cherry seeds per year. The oil is used in making cosmetics, the residue of the kernel is ground up for fertilizer, and the shells make good fuel."

In this country we produce in average years, 2,400,-000,000 pounds of animal fats and yet this enormous total from butter, lard, tallow, and the like is almost equaled by our production of cottonseed oil, 1,500,000,000 pounds. The once-despised cottonseed, a nuisance to everybody, now yields the South great wealth from its linters (short cotton fibers), its oil, and its residual oil cake, a good protein food for stock. Of course we import some olive oil for salad dressings yet we use much of our own refined cottonseed oil and corn oil, as well as peanut oil, for the same purpose. There was not enough lard to meet the demand for a solid cooking fat so chemistry came to the rescue, taught industry how to "harden" liquid fats just enough to resemble lard in consistency and appearance. As a result hydrogen gas is coaxed by a trace of nickel catalyst to add on to the fat molecules of liquid cottonseed oil to do the work of 7,000,000 hogs. In other words 400,000,000 pounds of hydrogenated or hardened fat of vegetable origin is annually prepared for the American kitchen.

Could you have imagined that a bean full of fat would have caused many millions of Chinese to migrate great distances with untold suffering and would threaten to plunge mankind into another world war? The prize worth fighting for, in the minds of two or three nations, was the wonderful soy bean of Manchuria. Every year 4,000,000 tons of soy beans are produced in Manchuria for food and soap-making. No other soil and climate suits quite so well this desirable plant. The oil is now substituted for part of the linseed oil in paints, with great improvement of the product. The meal left after removal of the fat is rich in protein, an excellent stock food, or fertilizer. The entire bean may be cooked for human food since it furnishes protein, carbohydrate, and fat. Ground to a milk in water it is coagulated into a curd or even worked into the form of a cheese of great value in the human diet. Bean sprouts furnish much-needed vitamins to the

Chinese table. Finally the plant is a legume, adding nitrogen from the air in available form to the soil. Is it any wonder that American farmers now produce 750,000 tons of oil and much stock food from this new crop?

Speaking of the Orient, there is China-wood oil or tung oil to be considered—to the extent of 100,000,000 pounds imported yearly by the United States. It is a much faster drying oil than linseed oil for varnishes, paints, lithograph inks, and linoleum. The varnish on ships as well as that on floors or tables so often pictured in thrilling advertisements representing playful children pouring boiling water on the aforesaid polished tables or floors, is made with tung oil. Evidently we must have it.

In Florida they think we, or rather they, must grow the Oriental tung tree. They have been planting and testing for thirty years and have finally unhorsed all skeptics by producing purer tung oil at a lower cost than is possible in China. These Florida enthusiasts remind us that we import as much linseed oil as we produce, that we can easily substitute tung oil for a large part of this foreign fat and save America $50,000,000 yearly, and that 500,000 acres of Florida land may profitably be set out in the tung trees which produce beautiful pink blooms and rich greasy nuts. This pardonable state pride seems to be well grounded, or should we say rooted, in sound experiments, for in a recent year our Gulf Coast produced over 5,000,000 pounds of tung oil.

Now comes another oil claiming a place in the sun and a seat in the circle of the family of fats. None other than whale oil, once the most popular illuminant before it was driven out of favor by kerosene and electricity. The dying whale industry that in its heyday made Nantucket and New Bedford famous in every port of the seven seas has suddenly and recently revived—but not in Nantucket. Norway and England annually send out over 200 whaling boats, equipped with electrical harpoons, to bring back 3,000,000 barrels (400 pounds each) of whale oil along with enough other by-products to total a $30,000,000 catch. The largest of the floating factories killed 1400 whales one year and brought back 18,000 tons of oil, valued at $2,250,000. Whale oil soap, smelling to high heaven, has long been in disfavor with the insect enemies of rose bushes but the needs of rose growers did not threaten to exterminate the race of whales.

Now things have come to a pretty pass, for, as the *Chicago Journal of Commerce* remarks, "When the lookout on a

Fig. 64. "Thar she blows!" is still the warning cry from the lookout on a whaler.

ship plying the South Atlantic cries, 'Thar she blows,' his voice is heard in Iowa." Modern hydrogenation of whale oil quiets the loud-smelling odor and makes this once-despised fat look like lard. In fact, the product sells in Europe as a lard substitute and is worked into their oleomargarine. The painful competition abroad with Iowa lard occasioned the surprising observation just quoted. The American dairyman, also, has his troubles, trying to hold down the production of margarine as a butter substitute. He suspects that a large portion of the 330,000,000 pounds of coconut fat imported into the United States annually comes for no good purpose, that it finally appears as "nut margarine."

Fats, even in coffee, have a tendency to oxidize in air and become rancid. Now we learn that lard containing 5 per cent of oat flour keeps much better, and that a very little preserves the aroma of coffee.

* * *

Soaps are comparatively modern, at least as far as extensive use goes. In the days of Cleopatra there was much oiling of beautiful skins with fats but, in the absence of soaps, perfumes had to be depended upon to distract attention.

Then, possibly, some well-greased person rubbed ashes on his person in a frenzy of remorse for some offense and, later, cooled himself with water. A little rubbing to remove the ashes and fatty oil astonished all beholders by the production of soap suds. With a final plunge in the Nile (or was it the Ganges?) the cleanest man in history (up to that date) proudly stepped forth. Soap, the yardstick of civilization, had been discovered. As your own great grandmother knew, the "lye" (potassium carbonate, K_2CO_3) of wood ashes cooked up with fats produces soap.

There was, it must be admitted, a little delay in pushing this great discovery just as there is still found, in some sections of the world, a certain reluctance to profit by it. Now in the United States synthetic detergents claim 64 per cent of the market once held by soaps.

It is a comparatively simple matter to make soap yet we do it with the grand gesture. Fats by the car load are boiled for days with caustic soda in three-story kettles holding 500,000 pounds of soap. Addition of common salt forces the soap into a thick upper layer, leaving below a brine containing the valuable glycerine set free in the reaction. Here is a sketchy scenario of the action:

Fat + sodium hydroxide → glycerine + a soap
Glyceryl oleate   NaOH $C_3H_5(OH)_3$ sodium oleate

Liquid fats and potassium hydroxide (or carbonate) yield softer soaps while the harder soaps are made from sodium hydroxide (or carbonate) and the firmer fats. If we tell you that there is not enough lard or tallow to meet the demand for hard soap what would you suggest as a substitute? Yes, your idea is good, even brilliant. Force hydrogen to unite with cheap and abundant cottonseed oil, for example, until a solid fat results, then cook this with sodium hydroxide until a firm soap separates. Fortunately somebody thought of this many years ago.

Soapless detergents are now in competition with soaps for nearly all general purposes. Long-chain fatty acids, such as those from coconut oil, are hydrogenated under high pressure and at elevated temperatures with a catalyst present. The — COOH group is reduced to the — CH_2OH group or, in other words, the acid becomes an alcohol. This alcohol is next sulfated (with sulfuric acid) and neutralized to yield sodium salts. Such products form a cleansing froth in hard water and in sea water and are useful also in aiding the uniform penetration of dye solutions in fabrics.

The glycerine set free in soap-making is a valuable by-product, useful in cosmetics, in keeping certain foods and other products moist, and in making nitroglycerine, and as an anti-freeze liquid for automobiles. It is sweet, has a definite food value, but, mark you, it is an alcohol.

That last statement, though true, was made merely to lead you into a consideration of alcohols in general. You know most about "grain alcohol" or ethyl alcohol or ethanol, to give it all its names. Yet there are many organic compounds also containing in each molecule a hydroxyl group, — OH, attached to a carbon radical such as CH_3 —, C_2H_5 —, C_3H_5 —, or more imposing groups of atoms with carbon at the center.

You have just learned that glycerine is a by-product when fats are converted into soaps but you may not have noticed that this non-intoxicating glycerine is technically an alcohol.

It is merely a matter of molecular structure as the following list shows.

CH_3OH	Methyl (wood) alcohol
C_2H_5OH	Ethyl (grain) alcohol
$C_3H_5(OH)_3$	Glycerine
R.OH	Almost any alcohol

In the last formula, a very general one, R — is used to represent CH_3 —, C_2H_5 —, or any carbon radical. These — OH groups seem to be greatly influenced by the company they keep. Attached to a metal as in NaOH, caustic soda, they break away, carrying an electric charge (they ionize) whenever the base is dissolved in water. Now if the dry voters could only arrange to have these — OH groups in ethyl alcohol, which has dissolved in water, break away from the ethyl group, picking up an electric charge in the act, there would be no prohibition problem. Whiskey would then taste like any alkali and its popularity would wane.

Obviously CH_3OH is the simplest alcohol possible and, we may add, the worst to drink, actually a poison. As one of the products of the dry distillation of wood it gets its name of wood alcohol, although chemists prefer to call it methyl alcohol or methanol. Since the war we have learned how to make it (under pressure and in the presence of a catalyst or coaxer) from water gas, which is nothing but a mixture of carbon monoxide and hydrogen.

$$CO + 2H_2 \rightarrow CH_3OH.$$

With these alcohols as points of departure we can prepare a multitude of useful compounds such as ethers, aldehydes, esters (of perfumes), organic acids, and ketones.

Note the importance of methyl alcohol alone as the starting point in the manufacture of formaldehyde. A mere trick of passing the vapors mixed with air over hot copper oxide.

$$CH_3OH + (O) \rightarrow H_2O + H \cdot CHO, \text{ formaldehyde.}$$

You would probably remain coldly indifferent to this product after one sniff but if your money were invested in a company making bakelite, the great synthetic plastic, your indifference would change to kindly indulgence. Formaldehyde is coupled to phenol from coal tar to form excellent lacquer material with great electrical insulating power, or molding powders that, mixed with fillers and heated, become strong resinous products. Laminated with cloth, bakelite is shaped into silent gears. You use it in telephone parts, switch plates, radio panels, in countless places to the extent of 100,000 tons annually in this country alone. This bakelite is a synthetic plastic.

Our synthetic plastic industry has grown rapidly, since the outstanding success of bakelite, to an annual production of over one million tons. Bakeland's original idea of coupling phenol with formaldehyde has been varied. Furfuraldehyde from oat hulls competes with formaldehyde. Phenol, in coupling with formaldehyde, has been replaced by protein (as with the casein of milk). The solid product is readily molded into useful forms by heat and pressure. Henry Ford substitutes soy-bean protein and is making from the product several parts of his car.

Urea condenses with formaldehyde to yield a new plastic called "beetle" which takes colors well, is not easily broken, and so finds use for tableware, etc.

Plywood, thin sheets of wood veneer, banded with waterproof plastic glue, has found extensive use in airplanes and is competing with thin metal sheets. Of course celluloid and its twin, cellulose acetate, are important in the plastic field and others will join.

There is so much discredit attached to ethyl alcohol that it is only fair to give it a little credit in passing. As servant, not as master, it is one of the best solvents in the laboratory and a starting point in the manufacture of dyes, lacquers, explosives, cosmetics, and medicines. Surgery without this alcohol, C_2H_5OH, would do without the great anesthetics ether, chloroform, and ethylene which are made from alcohol. When coal and oil are gone we can run our motors with this liquid for we can make it with every crop of starch, sugar, and cellulose. Nearly 200,000,000 gallons annually find legitimate use in industry. Recently the manufacture of common alcohol from the ethylene gas of petroleum refineries has begun to dispute the field with sugars and starch as sources. In the end the compulsory addition of alcohol to gasoline may not give the farmer the aid intended.

Now, in retrospect, see how easily you slipped from fats, through soaps and glycerine to an alcoholic end. No, not an end, for the various alcohols, like the benzene of coal tar, are but the beginning of an intricate and useful chemistry.

XXIV

NOW WHAT SHALL WE HAVE TO EAT?

EATING IS, or should be, such an artistic pleasure that it seems a pity to apply cold, scientific analysis to the gastronomic art. The mellow glow that accompanies a good dinner is slightly dimmed by too close a consideration of calories and proper tissue replacement.

However, between meals, we may risk nervous indigestion by analyzing our most effective diets. Suppose we learn our needs by ruthlessly thrusting a healthy specimen of *genus homo* into an adequate test tube and analyzing him.

The chemist's report indicates protein, largely found in the victim's muscles. Upon taking the complex protein molecules apart we find them built up of about thirty smaller molecules called amino acids, only one (cystine) or two containing any sulfur. Otherwise they all contain nitrogen, carbon, hydrogen, and oxygen. It might seem quite safe to eat any one vegetable or animal protein food in order to build up or replace our own worn-out muscle but that is not a safe rule. The protein of white bread, for example, lacks the amino acid, lysine, and must be supplemented by other proteins containing this essential.

A number of proteins should be selected from lean meat, milk, cheese, cereals, eggs, peas, and beans.

Analysis of our healthy individual reports fat, enough to make muscles play smoothly upon each other and to act as a balance wheel on our energy supply. We would be wise to build up our own, not an obtrusive amount, of course, from butter, vegetable salad oils, soy beans, the usual animal fats, and from the carbohydrates, sugar and starch.

As to carbohydrates we are relieved to learn that there was very little undigested sugar in the healthy young man just analyzed. He may have been killed by chemistry but he certainly did not die of diabetes. We do learn, however, that there was some glycogen, a carbohydrate, in his body, most of it in the liver. He used up a lot of it in his violent efforts to resist placement in the test tube but that was to be expected. Glycogen is our quick source of energy when fury or fear puts fight in our fists or flight in our heels.

And yet scientific observation shows us that we have for years instinctively and profitably eaten a good deal of carbohydrate food. Why? The flippant but adequate answer is that we are firing the furnace with sugars and starch, even with fats. Not a bad answer at all for if you burn your breakfast pat of butter in a calorimeter which meticulously counts the calories of heat evolved, and then eat an equal amount of butter, the heat liberated in calorimeter and body will be practically the same. This startling fact was learned by Atwater who caged a young freshman in a very large calorimeter well equipped with thermometers and all the comforts of home, fed him weighed amounts of certain foods, had him exercise and rest, while all the time measuring the heat evolved from the young man's body. We dare not state that such experiments, from which our food-calorie tables were developed, became the fad but we do know that at Pennsylvania State College they—the professors, not the students—put a cow in one of these animal calorimeters. Moreover the results were valuable to science.

Our analyst, whom we have kept waiting while we discoursed on cows, now informs us that the bones of our specimen apparently owed their rigidity to calcium phosphate and some carbonate. But we are not ostriches, we can not get this calcium phosphate by eating cheap phosphate rock from Florida or Tunis. Experience has taught us that we can utilize calcium best as it is found combined in milk, cheese, oysters, eggs, raw cabbage, whole-wheat bread, beans, walnuts, chocolate, fruits, and vegetables.

The phosphorus, to be utilized, must come from its organic

FOOD SOURCES OF MINERAL ELEMENTS
(Adapted from Sherman)

	Calcium	Phos-phorus	Iron	Copper	Man-ganese
Almonds	+++	+++	+++	+++	+++
Beans (dried)	++	+++	+++	+++	++
Beans (fresh string)	+	+	++	+	+
Beef (lean)	+	+++	++	+	
Blueberries	+	+	+		+++
Broccoli	+++	+	++		
Brussels sprouts	+	++	++		
Cauliflower	++	+	+	+	+
Cheese	+++	+++	++		+
Chocolate	++	+++	++		+++
Collards	+++	+	+++		
Corn (sweet)		++	+		+
Dandelion greens	+	+	++		
Dates	++	+	++	+	+++
Fish	+	++	+ or ++	+	
Eggs	+	+++	++	+	
Flour (buckwheat)	+	++	++		+++
Flour (whole wheat)	+	+++	++	+	+++
Flour (white)	+	++	++	+	+
Huckleberries	+	+	+		+++
Kale	+++	+	++		+
Lentils	++	+++	+++	+++	
Lettuce	+	+	+	+	+
Liver	+	+++	+++		
Nuts	++	+++	++		
Oatmeal	+	+++	++		+++
Oysters	+	++	+++		
Peanuts	++	+++	++		
Peas (fresh)	+	++	++		
Potatoes	+	+	+	+	+
Spinach	++	+	++	+	+
Turnip greens	+++	+	+++	+	++

+ Contains the element.   ++ Good source.   +++ Excellent source.

compounds in milk, cheese, eggs, beef, walnuts, chocolate, fruits, and vegetables.

The good red blood of our victim owed its color and its ability to carry oxygen from the lungs all over the body to a complex iron compound called hemoglobin, so we are wise to get our own iron from spinach, egg yolk, lentils, liver, kidney, whole-wheat bread, oatmeal, beef, oysters, raisins, and chocolate. The old-fashioned "spring tonic" of sulfur and molasses really did your father some good because of the iron in very crude molasses. It is now asserted that the action of iron in the body is stimulated by traces of copper.

It seems probable that the endocrine glands are in some way related to manganese. There is evidence, too, that the pituitary gland is dependent upon the proper amount of manganese in the body.

As a final triumph of efficiency our conscientious analyst reports the presence of 25 milligrams, a trifling weight, of organic iodine, over half of it in the thyroid gland. Obviously our victim had no goiter enlarging his neck, probably because his diet furnished him enough combined iodine or because, as a growing boy, he was required by his family physician to take two grams of sodium iodide twice yearly. It is a fact that in wide areas far from the wind-blown salt spray of the sea, there is a deficiency in the iodine content of water and vegetables. Consequently sea food is a corrective as well as a delight in the diet. South Carolina tells the world to eat its string beans and other vegetables for their unusually rich iodine content.

Now that we have learned what we must eat, and why, we might, with profit, consider how we digest it. Plain common sense convinces you that the insoluble food (only the sugar and salt of food are soluble) can not be carried through the walls of the intestines and along the blood stream to every fiber of tissue unless converted into soluble products by some sort of chemical action. Those helpful catalysts, the enzymes, of our digestive juices save the day and the dinner.

Read this compact story of digestion, and read it another day, and still another.

Protein
- Partly broken down in the stomach by *pepsin.*
- Completely torn apart in small intestine by *trypsin* and *erepsin.*
- Products carried through intestinal wall to all parts of body.
- Products built up again into muscle.

Fats
- Emulsified into minute droplets by bile in the small intestine.
- Split by *lipase* into fatty acids and glycerine.
- Products pass through intestinal wall.
- Transported and built into fats again.
- Oxidized as a fuel for energy.

Carbohydrates
$\begin{cases}\text{Starch partly digested by } ptyalin \text{ of saliva.}\\ \text{Starch converted (by } amylase \text{ of intestine) into malt sugar}\\ \quad \text{(maltose).}\\ \text{Maltose} \rightarrow \text{glucose (by } maltase).\\ \text{Glucose passes through intestinal wall.}\\ \text{Glucose oxidized as fuel for energy.}\\ \text{Cane sugar split by } sucrase \text{ of the intestine into glucose}\\ \quad \text{and fructose.}\end{cases}$

Yet with all this knowledge of your body needs (including water) you may waste away unless your diet includes some half dozen vital chemicals in almost unweighable traces, the **Vitamins**. They are well named. The first observed deficiency disease, caused by their lack, was sailor's scurvy, which killed off many of Captain Cook's exploring crew. That was in the tough old times before Appert, the Frenchman, taught the world how to preserve food by canning (although Appert had to use glass bottles) and when voyages lasted longer than fresh food.

When it was learned that lemon juice cured scurvy, the science of vitamins came within reach, but was not quite grasped. The world waited—and suffered thereby—until Eykman in Java (about 1897) and Funk in London (1912) led us to suspect the existence of these accessory food substances. They cured beriberi, a disease common with poor natives using polished rice as their main diet, by adding the polishings to the same deficient diet. Something vital was in those polishings.

Vitamin A, soluble in fats but found in only a few of them, is essential in building up resistance to disease, and in maintaining growth in the young. Sherman insists that we must eat several times the minimum amount that barely keeps us going in order to live at our best.

The richest sources are the liver oils of halibut, cod, and some other fish, butter, egg yolk, green leafy vegetables, tomatoes, carrots, peas, and yellow corn.

In the last few years we have definitely proved that some plants secrete carotene, $C_{40}H_{56}$, a yellow to red substance easily oxidized and biologically ruined in air, and that animals (yourself included) convert this carotene into vitamin A. So you thrive on spinach as well as on butter. Of course the cow converts carotene of green grass into the vitamin A of butter while the cod eats a smaller denizen of the deep which in turn

(*Calif. Fruit Growers Exchange*)

FIG. 65. Vizcaino's Crew.

"We had come as far as the bay of Monterey, where the Indians signalled us with smoke. We did not enter it because the state of our health was so bad. The mouths of all were sore, and their gums were swollen larger than their teeth, so that they could hardly drink water . . . The General ordered that we go to the Islands of Mazatlan . . . The alcalde mayor . . . aided him with . . . fruits and vegetables . . . Such was the efficacy of the fruit that within six days there was not a single person whose mouth was not healed." From the diary of Sebastian Vizcaino's expedition along the California coast. 1602-3.

ate plant life of the sea. The color of carrots is wholly due to carotene, in great dilution.

Vitamin B_1, the lack of which causes beriberi, should be supplied by any varied diet and yet when appetite, digestion, and general vigor fail it may be well to take tablets of the vitamin itself (thiamin chloride). It may also cure your insomnia and increase your ability to work.

Vitamin C (ascorbic acid) cures scurvy, contributes to the health of gums and teeth, aids wound healing and, in daily doses of at least 200 milligrams, often helps in hay fever and some other allergies. The body level is lowered by infections. Citrus fruits, raw cabbage and raw green leafy vegetables are excellent sources; tomatoes are good. Oxidation losses in storage and in cooking are serious.

Vitamin D is the magical catalyst that enables growing children to store calcium phosphate in the bones. A lack of it, or a lack of good outdoor sunshine, dooms the child to rickets. It was a brilliant line of research that proved that ultra-violet light of outdoor sunshine or of mercury-arc lamps converts the ergosterol of the skin into vitamin D or its equivalent. Still more brilliant was the discovery that ergosterol secreted by yeast can be irradiated by ultra-violet light to produce "Viosterol," synthetic vitamin D. This captured sunshine saves the expense of a winter trip to Florida or to the high Alps and gives to poor children as sturdy bones as those of the rich. It must be urged, however, that viosterol is not a complete substitute for cod liver oil which contains vitamin A as well as D.

Vitamin A (isolated at Oberlin College) is now synthesized commercially so compact capsules are available as a dietary supplement.

Vitamin B_{12} is invaluable in the treatment of pernicious anemia.

Vitamin G, of lean meat, milk, spinach, and kale, promotes general health and long life and helps "niacin" cure pellagra. Riboflavin is its chemical name.

These vitamins are actual chemicals needed, like hormones, in minute amounts to regulate the body processes. Several, like A, B, and C, have been isolated and synthesized.

You may wonder how we learn whether a given food contains a certain vitamin or not. Several young white rats are fed for weeks a diet lacking only the vitamin in question until they are definitely sick or losing weight. Then the food to be tested is added to the ration and general health and

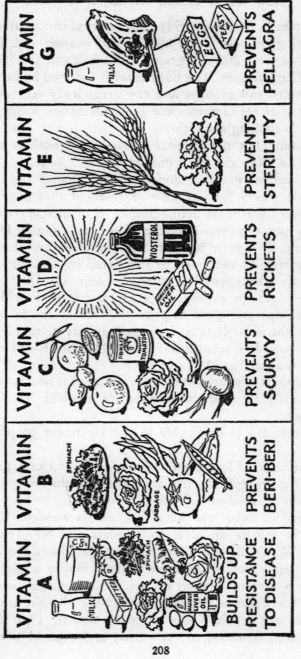

FIG. 66. Vitamin chart. Now we give niacin the pellagra credit once assigned to G. Both vitamins occur together in the "B complex."

growth observed. The results are so valuable to the human race that a monument, preferably white, ought to be erected in honor of the white rat.

We urge you to type, quite accurately, the following vitamin chart and post it conspicuously in the kitchen. It may keep the doctor away.

FOOD SOURCES OF VITAMINS

	"A"	"B"	"C"	"G"
Apples	+	++	++	++
Asparagus	+ to ++	+++	++	+++
Bananas	++	++	++	++
Beans (fresh string)	++	++	++	?
Beans (navy)	+	++		
Beef (lean)	+	++	+	++
Berries (raspberries)	++	+	+++	?
Butter	+++			
Cabbage (raw)	+	++	+++	++
Cabbage (cooked 20 minutes)	+	++	++	++
Cantaloupe	++	++	+++	++
Carrots	+++	++	++	++
Cheese	+++			?
Chinese cabbage ("celery cabbage")	++	++	+++	++
Collards	+++	++	++	++
Cream	+++	++	+	+++
Eggs	+++	++		+++
Grapefruit	+	++	+++	++
Kale	+++	+	++	+++
Kidney	++	++	+	+++
Lemons	+	++	+++	++
Lettuce	++	++	++	++
Liver	+++	++	+	+++
Milk (fresh)	+++	++	++	+++
Milk powder	++	++	+	+++
Oranges	+	++	+++	++
Oysters	++	++	+	++
Peaches (raw)	++	++	++	?
Peas (fresh)	++	++	+++	+
Peppers (green)	++	++	+++	?
Potatoes	+	++	++	++
Spinach (fresh)	+++	+	++	+++
Spinach (canned)	+++	+	++	+++
Sweet potatoes	+++	++	++	?
Tomatoes (fresh or canned)	++	++	+++	++
Turnip greens	+++	++	+++	++
Turnips (white)	+	++	++	++
Yeast		+++		+++

+ Contains the vitamin. ++ Good source. +++ Excellent source.

The balanced ration requires intelligent selection, including a certain degree of restraint. The average business man needs daily enough food to furnish him from 2500 to 3000 large calories of heat while a laboring man may well demand nearly twice as much. For the business man eating wisely the sources of energy might be distributed as follows:

$$\left.\begin{array}{l} \text{70 grams protein} \\ \text{400 grams carbohydrate} \\ \text{80 grams fat} \end{array}\right\} = \textbf{2600 Cal.}$$

If you care to count your own calories base them upon these values:

$$\text{Fuel values} \left\{\begin{array}{l} \text{1 gram fat} = \text{9 Cal.} \\ \text{1 gram protein} = \text{4 Cal.} \\ \text{1 gram carbohydrate} = \text{4 Cal.} \end{array}\right.$$

Fats and carbohydrates are burned in the body furnace to yield carbon dioxide and water while the protein yields urea and other products. It is approximately true that a man daily gets as much energy out of his food as his automobile gets from a pint of gasoline.

A varied diet stressing milk (or cheese) and vegetables is best. Sherman demands a daily pint of milk for adults and a quart for growing children. Rose expresses contempt for the ignorant fancies "that protein and starch must never be eaten together and that fruit and starchy foods are incompatible." Professor Sherman is convinced that man may live, and live well, to 77 years, if he gets an abundance of vitamins A and G, a good allowance of protein, and a favorable balance between calcium and phosphorus.

Thanks to transportation aided by refrigeration our winter diet has been marvelously enriched with fresh vegetables. Head lettuce and spinach with their life-saving vitamins and mineral salts are always within the financial reach of the majority of people. Over 73,000 tons of oysters (not including shells) rich in iodine, iron, glycogen, and copper, are brought to town and city, fresh and wholesome, during an average year.

The "ubiquitous tin can of America" as Europeans love to call it, has been a blessing to the public with its invaluable contents of tomatoes, fruits and variety of vegetables.

The next great addition to our diet must be the soy-bean products which have carried the Chinese along for centuries. Manchuria growing over 4,000,000 tons annually of this bean had become a prize worth fighting for. This soy bean with its twenty per cent of very digestible fat, forty per cent of excellent protein, its rich content of both water-soluble and fat-soluble vitamins, of phosphorus, calcium, and magnesium, deserves a prominent place on the American table. The Chinese grind the bean to a milk which they coagulate with magnesium chloride or calcium sulfate. The cheese-like cake then obtained by pressing is called bean curd or "tofu" and a delicious and highly digestible food it makes. An international drive to teach people how to use the soy bean is now on, even in Russia. A flour that will not grow rancid is available, in fact, already used in this country by bakers and ice-cream manufacturers. Soy sauce aids digestion, possibly even when spiced to make Worcestershire sauce.

Rumania, encouraged by Germany, developed a great soy-bean industry in its province of Bessarabia, selling 1,000,000 tons a year to Germany. Russia's desire to appropriate Bessarabia was, in part at least, based on those wonderful beans, so valuable as army rations.

NOTE. Remember that in night driving your life may depend upon having an adequate reserve of vitamin A to regenerate quickly the visual purple of your eye, bleached by headlight glare.

Man's friend, the white rat, deserves a monument.

XXV

SHALL WE HAVE MEDICINES AND ANESTHETICS TO ORDER?

BACTERIA HAVE always been masters of men, sweeping them off by millions as with the Black Death of the Middle Ages or the virulent form of flu that scourged the earth in 1918, filling them with fears of the wrath of the gods, crippling the mighty Roman Empire, and cowing the races into a sense of helplessness not yet overcome.

It was a Spartan struggle in the dark, from man's viewpoint, this warfare between man and the vindictive types of bacteria, and the doctrine of the survival of the fittest was accepted as inevitable. Within less than a century, however, the tide has noticeably turned as man has learned to recognize and understand his enemy.

We owe a wealth of gratitude to the scientific amateur, Leeuwenhoek, for constructing a primitive microscope in 1685 and detecting with it "little beasties" in a drop of dirty water. Here was the first human being in Creation to see bacteria, discovering for the world an inner infinity destined to rival the outer infinity of cosmos revealed by the telescope. Leeuwenhoek showed the way, but none followed for over a century and a half until Pasteur the chemist laid well the foundations of bacteriology through his studies of diseases of wine and beer.

It took a Pasteur to show us, between 1860 and 1864, that heating wine in closed glass bottles to 50° C.—60° C. for a short period destroyed the yeasts and bacteria responsible for souring. The resulting prevention of disease by pasteurization of milk has had far-reaching effects on the health of our race. Pasteur advanced to further triumphs with his scientific attack on anthrax and rabies and paved the way for Koch and the other brilliant leaders in medical research. According to Dr. W. J. Mayo, "The epochal studies of the chemist, Pasteur, have been of greater service to mankind than those of any other human being."

Then came Lister's tremendous discovery in 1867 that solutions of carbolic acid did much to prevent the usual infec-

B. & L. Co.

FIG. 67. Leeuwenhoek shows his wife the first bacteria ever seen, thanks to his crude microscope (1685).

tions of surgical wounds. Lister handed over to the chemist the problem of making newer and better antiseptics and the chemist has responded with a great variety. Before Lister's day, to open a man's abdomen was practically to sign his death warrant. Now we accept the surgeon's elaborate antiseptic precautions as a matter of course. What terrible mortality there must have been in Cæsar's armies from infected wounds!

The full realization of Pasteur's magnificent contributions to the war on bacteria would never have been possible but for the discovery of aniline dyes. (The amazing Ripley might well have used this statement in his "Believe It or Not.") To quote Dr. William H. Welch, Dean of American medicine, "Who could have dreamed in 1856 that Sir William Perkin's production of the first aniline dye should be an essential link in the development of modern biology and therefore in the

Hercules Powder Co.

FIG. 68. Gone are the days when cobwebs were applied to
open wounds.

crusade against tuberculosis and other infectious diseases? As Robert Koch has said, it would have been quite impossible for him to have developed his methods and made his discoveries without the possession of selective dyes for staining bacteria, and no other class of coloring agents has been discovered which can serve as substitutes for the anilines in this regard."

The rapid rise of organic chemistry in the second half of the nineteenth century to the great triumphs of organic synthesis came just in time to meet the demands of medicine. To separate, purify, and analyze the potent hormones of ductless glands is an invitation to the chemist to synthesize them for more extended use, and to improve upon them. How splendidly was this realized with thyroxine "the chemical regulator" secreted by the thyroid gland. The synthetic thyroxine, given to the world in 1927, restored childish cretins and idiots to the normal type just as well as did the natural hormone. Adrenalin, a hormone present in the adrenal glands, powerful in raising blood pressure and in helping us to meet body emergencies, has likewise been copied perfectly by the synthetic chemist.

Late in 1933 came the announcement that from certain glands there had been separated a hormone capable of quickly restoring to mothers the lactation function whenever the infant had to be weaned for lack of the beneficent mother's milk. So potent is this hormone that it developed, rather slowly, the mammary glands of a tomcat and caused a considerable flow of milk. The sociological inferences from this remarkable experiment are almost revolutionary.

Insulin, a palliative but not a cure in diabetes, was separated along with other chemicals from animal pancreas by Banting and Best in 1922. Years later it was obtained in pure crystalline form by Abel and shown to be $C_{45}H_{69}O_{14}N_{11}S \cdot 3H_2O$. This amazingly heavy and complex molecule has so far defied laboratory synthesis but success is certain. Today it is the sex hormones, chemical activators and regulators, that engage the attention of many scientists. Were Ponce de León alive his interest in Florida real estate would undoubtedly be less than his interest in chemical laboratories.

The laboratory shelf has been called upon to furnish carbon tetrachloride as a cure for hookworm, the "disease of backwardness and laziness afflicting millions of people." Ancient Egypt suffered from this disease and half the population of the earth lives in areas where it is prevalent. As late as 1909 two million people in our own South were depressed and weakened by hookworm but great strides in its conquest have been made since that date. "With carbon tetrachloride the field workers of the International Health Board of the Rockefeller Foundation have cured many millions of people suffering from this disease." (*Abel.*) Hexylresorcinol, the kidney antiseptic, is now coming into use as a safe and apparently effective remedy for hookworm. The economic gain to the world should be almost incalculable.

Life in the tropics and sub-tropics is safe only with eternal vigilance against such enemies as mosquitoes carrying fever, and tsetse flies inoculating with sleeping sickness at every bite. Malaria claims a million deaths and a hundred million sufferers every year as its toll of the race. Quinine, an excellent specific for malaria, has been used for a century and is now supported by synthetic atabrine.

Ehrlich's success with arsphenamine, popularly called "606," in relieving the social scourge, syphilis, led to the preparation of many other organic compounds of arsenic, some of them valuable against syphilis and various tropical diseases. Carrying the chemical analogy a little farther, organic compounds of antimony (an element somewhat resembling arsenic) have been used with encouraging results. African sleeping sickness may yield to the complicated organic chemical called "Antrycide" and to some of the arsenicals and antimonials.

The observation that natives in the Orient ate the fatty nut of the chaulmoogra tree as a remedy for leprosy—with disastrous results to digestion and an occasional gain against the disease—led doctors and chemists to extract the peculiar fat and to try it as a treatment. The virtue lay in the fat. Next the peculiar fatty acids were separated from the fat and united with various alcoholic groups. The benefits remained and some of the ill effects disappeared. Now that the organic chemist has discovered the part of the molecule exerting curative effects he may be expected to try many variations in chemical constitution. In the meantime derivatives of the sulfones and other substances will be tested.

Cancer research is making demands upon the chemist for a new dye that will differentiate in its staining action between cancer cells and abnormal cells that are not cancer. At present diagnosis in the early stages of the disease is the best weapon, and an effective one.

A very great modern contribution to chemotherapy is sulfanilamide which, with sulfadiazene and other related sulfa drugs, has proved invaluable in combating pneumonia and other dangerous infections.

$$
\begin{array}{cc}
\text{HC} \quad \text{CH} & \text{CH} \quad \text{CH} \\
\text{HC} \diagdown\!\!\!\diagup \text{CH} & \text{H}_2\text{N.C.} \diagdown\!\!\!\diagup \text{C.SO}_2\text{NH}_2 \\
\text{CH} \quad \text{CH} & \text{CH} \quad \text{CH} \\
\text{Benzene} & \text{Sulfanilamide}
\end{array}
$$

"No single discovery in medicine has been more conducive to the progress of medical sciences as a whole than the discovery of general anesthesia." (*A. B. Luckhardt.*) And yet until 1842, when Crawford W. Long, a village doctor in Georgia, first used ether in a minor operation, the world was resigned to the usual agonies of surgical operations.

This was a costly delay from 1799 when young Sir Humphrey Davy, after trying "laughing gas" or nitrous oxide (N_2O) on himself, wrote:

"As nitrous oxide in its extensive operation appears capable of destroying physical pain, it may probably be used to advantage during surgical operations in which no great effusion of blood takes place."

Yet all the world did with nitrous oxide was to attend public exhibitions where volunteers took the gas and amused the audience with their hysterical antics. "Ether frolics" were common years before the serious use of this merciful anesthetic. The first public demonstration of the use of ether in general anesthesia was staged by Morton and the surgeon Warren, October 17, 1846, at the Massachusetts General Hospital, Boston. On that day "surgical anesthesia became the priceless heritage of the civilized world."

The use of general anesthetics is merciful but their value goes far beyond mercy. Serious abdominal operations, brain surgery and chest surgery would be almost impossible without them. The search for better anesthetics goes on.

Chloroform was used later, although more in Europe than in America, and finally nitrous oxide came into its own (administered with oxygen) as a common aid to the surgeon. It has many advantages. The introduction of ethylene, C_2H_4, by Luckhardt and Carter in 1923, was another important step forward. Reasoning by analogy, the somewhat similar gases, propylene, C_3H_6, and acetylene, C_2H_2, have been tested and shown to have anesthetic merit but their use is minor as yet.

Nerve-blocking by injections of pentathol sodium is widely used by surgeons because it is very effective and at the same time free from causing nausea.

The use of local anesthetics has greatly aided many special types of surgery but it was an unknown art before 1884 when cocaine was first used in an eye operation. The rather toxic qualities of this drug and its habit-creating property led chemists to discover the part of the molecule essential to anesthesia. Of course the structure of the entire molecule had first to be made clear, a mere matter of several years of research. By building up new molecules based upon different groups of atoms observed in the molecule of cocaine and by testing these products it was at last learned that the anesthetic merit was confined to the upper right hand corner of the following diagram, as marked off by a dotted line:

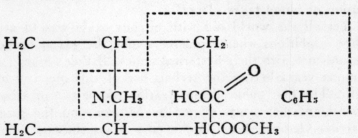

Such research led to the manufacture and use of procaine (novocaine) in 1905, a local anesthetic far superior to cocaine, less toxic and with no habit-forming properties. Butyn and many others have followed. Similar studies of essential groups have improved hypnotics, one of the latest groups of value being the amyl ethyl barbituric acids. Each group in the molecule produces its own effect, insuring in the molecule a sort of balance of power.

From all this we see that medicine asks chemistry "to disclose the true nature of toxins of disease, of antitoxins and vaccines, of all the substances secreted by bacteria; to make dyes for selective staining of bacteria; to prepare anesthetics, antiseptics and alleviative and curative drugs." A large order, yet it is being carried out with brilliant success.

Lehn and Fink

FIG. 69. During the Franco-Prussian War the surgeon Velpeau cried out in despair, "A pinprick is a door open to death!"

Dr. Will and Dr. Charley Mayo told us that the average life of mankind in the time of Queen Elizabeth I was 20 years. Today, the average is 67 years for man and 69 for woman. The prospect is that the life of man will soon reach three score and ten in this country.

"There are many ways by which men rise to eminence among their fellows. It has always seemed to me, however, that when the Great Assize is held and the roll of the foremost names in history is called, the high places will be held not by the great captains who have caused the very earth to tremble beneath the feet of their marching hosts; not by the statesmen who have raised and ruined states and empires; not by the great philanthropists who have turned their talents and resources to the service of mankind; not even by the writers, poets, musicians, and creative artists who have made the subtle beauty of their dreams the living inspiration and the pleasure of less gifted men. Before all these I think I must rank the hosts of the great discoverers who have rolled away the mists of ignorance that blinded human sight. Great explorers and scientists like Archimedes, Copernicus, Galileo, Columbus, Magellan, Newton, Harvey, Watts, Lavoisier, and many more, both known and unknown to fame, will be the first names called; and standing near the head of the line will be the chemist, Louis Pasteur, whose labors divided all medical history into two periods, that which preceded and that which followed his discoveries." (*John W. Davis.*)

To this eloquent tribute we might appropriately add a statement by Dr. Charles M. A. Stine: "Modern medicine is largely applied chemistry. The human body is fundamentally a complex and highly integrated chemical machine."

One of the latest triumphs in medicine is the discovery of penicillin and many other antibiotics in molds. The chemist isolates them for medical use.

Thousands of molds in samples of soils from all over the world are now being tested for possible antibiotic content.

XXVI

LET THE YEASTS, MOLDS, AND BACTERIA DO THE WORK

THE TIRELESS micro-organisms have been doing much of the world's work for some thousands of years without getting proper credit. True, the ancient Egyptians knew how to make bread with the aid of yeasts; and the fermentations involved in the making of wine, beer, and vinegar were widely known in very ancient times. Known and used but not understood.

Tools were needed for such study and with bacteria, at least, nothing could be learned until Leeuwenhoek conceived a crude microscope in the 17th century. Yet it was not until Pasteur, less than a century ago, laid well the foundations of the science of the micro-organisms—the bacteria, yeasts, and molds—that any considerable advance in such study became possible. Some pioneering genius and some new tool are generally found to be responsible for new life in any science.

We are becoming micro-organism conscious, in a somewhat fearful way perhaps, as we think of our bacterial enemies, and of the spoilage of foods. Yet within recent years we have learned to harness these lowly little plants to compel them to do more of our work. In the United States alone the food industry achieves the staggering total of twenty billion dollars, and of this ten per cent is in some way or another touched by fermentation processes. If you doubt this, think of the production of bread, cheese, sauerkraut, pickles, and vinegar as good illustrations.

To strengthen the case for the micro-organism it may be contended that, without soil bacteria, the dead animals and plants of past ages would encumber the earth, making life impossible or, at least, intolerable for us.

Now at the risk of seeming to change the subject suddenly, even violently, we ask you to recall all the catalysts you have ever met. Perhaps you doubt your ability to recognize a catalyst on sight. Will it help to be assured that they are the good Samaritans of chemistry, our friendly helpers? Whenever a chemical reaction needs jazzing up or we become impatient for dividends from the chemical industry in which we have invested our money we call in a relatively small

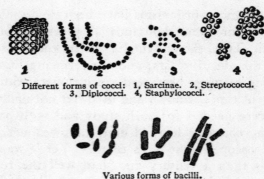

Different forms of cocci: 1, Sarcinae. 2, Streptococci.
3, Diplococci. 4, Staphylococci.

Various forms of bacilli.

Various forms of spirilla.

Parke Davis Co.

FIG. 70. Various forms of bacteria.

amount of platinum, or iron, or nickel or vanadium oxide or one of a very long list of chemicals known to accelerate the speed of certain reactions. To be a genuine **catalyst** a little must go a long way, coaxing lazy molecules to react without itself being used up. You probably remember that the slow union of sulfur dioxide with oxygen is greatly speeded up when these gases are blown through some porous solid coated with dusty platinum. Sulfur trioxide is formed, and with the final addition of water, sulfuric acid is the product. With care a single batch of this catalytic platinum ought to work for years making thousands of tons of sulfuric acid.

We now believe that for every chemical reaction there exists (if we could only discover the right one) a catalyst, perhaps several of them. So far we have written of inorganic catalysts, metals or metallic compounds and all quite dead.

Now brace yourself for a great shock. You are quietly and modestly secreting within your own body some of the most efficient catalysts known, and in all probability have never boasted of your catalytic manufacturing skill. Your brand includes only carbon compounds such as the pepsin of the stomach juices, the lipase, trypsin, and maltase of the intestine. Now your guess that digestion waits not only upon appetite but upon the successful catalysis of food reactions seems to be correct. If you care to know, the catalysts secreted by animals and plants are called enzymes. Yes, plants are just as clever as we are. When a grain of corn sends out a sprout it gets into trouble at once. How can the insoluble starch of the grain, which at first supplies all the food, be transported by the juice of the growing leaflet? Just in the nick of time the sprouting grain manufactures a catalyst, a chemical called amylase, which helps convert the insoluble corn starch into the sugar called maltose. To make a thorough job of it, the sprout secretes a second enzyme to catalyze the change of maltose into the very soluble glucose.

Even those lower, simpler forms of plants called yeasts, molds, and bacteria secrete organic catalysts, the enzymes. Büchner killed yeast plants by grinding with sand in a mortar, extracted the juice and found that fermentations went on just as well with the dead juice as with the living yeast, so proving that fermentation did not depend directly upon life, that it was, in fact, purely chemical. As you remember, we can duplicate some of the achievements of enzymes with quite ordinary chemicals. A trace of any acid hydrolizes wet starch to glucose or splits cane sugar into glucose (dextrose) and levulose.

Note the reactions catalyzed by enzymes in the synthesis of alcohol.

1. Starch from grain converted into maltose by an enzyme in the malt of sprouted barley.

2. Maltose (a sugar) converted into glucose (a fermentable sugar) by an enzyme secreted by yeast.

3. Glucose fermented into alcohol and carbon dioxide by an enzyme (zymase) also secreted in the yeast plant.

$$\text{Glucose } C_6H_{12}O_6 \rightarrow 2CO_2 + 2C_2H_5OH, \text{ alcohol.}$$

It is a curious fact that cane sugar is not fermented into alcohol directly by the aid of zymase. It must, like starch, first be converted into fermentable sugars so the average bootlegger prefers to start with glucose.

The speed with which some of these enzymes work is amazing. Urease catalyzes the reaction between water and urea so efficiently that it produces 120 times its own weight of ammonia as a product every five minutes (at room temperature).

$$\text{Urea, } (NH_2)_2CO + H_2O \rightarrow CO_2 + 2NH_3, \text{ ammonia.}$$

Of course these yeasts must be fed and pampered, more or less. They work best in a slightly acid environment and are rather partial to their favorite temperatures. Unlike the higher orders of plants yeasts are unable to take the carbon of their tissues from atmospheric carbon dioxide so they must be fed sugar as the source of essential carbon. Pasteur proved that ammonium salts are vital to their health and growth and other workers learned that the phosphates and sulfates of potassium, magnesium, and calcium are stimulating.

This yeast culture may some day supplement agriculture on a vast scale. If overcrowding becomes desperate the yeast plant may be the salvation of the human race. Barnard asserts that:

"Thirty men working in a factory the size of a city block can produce in the form of yeast as much food as 1,000 farmers tilling 57,000 acres under ordinary agricultural conditions. To the chemist the Malthusian doctrine is but the sad reflection of a pessimistic world."

We chemists can synthesize ammonium salts from the nitrogen of the air but we are absolutely unable to utilize this inorganic nitrogen as food. However, the yeast plant can do so, in fact it converts it into good digestible protein of its tissues ready for cattle to eat. Perhaps some day we shall learn how to grow yeasts of delicious flavor and to treat them so that no injurious effects come from eating quantities of this food. Even now we eat a little yeast as a rich source of vitamins B and G and we separate from it on a factory scale considerable quantities of ergosterol, the parent of vitamin D.

It may strain your credulity to hint that armies might use yeasts as weapons but we shall risk it. In World War I Germany lacked enough fat to feed the nation, to make soap and to yield glycerine, the starting point in the manufacture of nitroglycerine. A yeast capable of fermenting common sugar into glycerine in great quantities was discovered and used, yielding 1,000 tons per month.

Possibly the average citizen believes he can do very well, thank you, without molds, associating them as he does with the green or blue or white whiskers often seen on spoiled bread, or fruit, or shoes discarded in moist weather. Yet it is to specially selected strains of molds that we owe the more or less delicate flavors of Camembert, Roquefort and similar cheeses.

The citric acid used in many "soft" drinks is now prepared in thousands of tons from cane sugar by the aid of a special mold. The lemon tree has found a rival. Quite recently Herrick and May have cultivated another mold able to convert glucose into gluconic acid. This rare acid once priced at $100 per pound may now be manufactured at a fraction of a dollar per pound but, as yet, the demand is small. Calcium gluconate, its salt, promises to become a better source of calcium in nutrition than other calcium compounds. In 1933 Ward and Lockwood of the United States Bureau of Chemistry found a mold, *Penicillium javanicum,* that converts glucose into fat within twelve days.

The importance of bacteria will be conceded without question as we think of their relation to disease, and yet friendly microbes are working hard for us. Long before man learned how to "fix" free atmospheric nitrogen into compounds available as plant food the nitrifying bacteria clustering on the roots of clover, alfalfa and other legumes were quietly doing the same thing, enriching the soil for the next crop.

Back in the gray mists of prehistoric times various strains of bacteria floating in the air fell into animal milk, fermented its sweetness into sourness, its milk sugar or lactose into lactic acid. Just when sauerkraut was first made with the help of lactic acid bacilli is not recorded but it is a venerable product. The modern farmer deliberately piles green corn fodder into a silo where "*lactobacillus*" ferments it to suit the taste of barnyard animals. Other acids besides lactic result, thanks to the action of about eight billion bacteria in each thimbleful of juice.

We are now interested in growing a vigorous flora of *bacillus acidophilus* in our own lower intestines in order to crowd out less friendly bacilli. This particular strain gets its energy from carbohydrates, preferably lactose or milk sugar, and forms harmless products such as lactic acid. This is the reason for the use of various soured-milk foods. The usual bacterial population of the lower intestine is an unmixed curse, getting its energy from protein waste products and forming the toxic amines, phenols, hydrogen sulfide, and other products responsible for "auto-intoxication." If plenty of carbohydrate reaches the lower intestine (not easy to manage) the putrefying bacteria may obtain their energy from this food instead of from protein with the great advantage that harmless chemical products result.

There is support for this view in the fact that lactic acid bacteria in sauerkraut and several other soured foods prevent decay and spoilage by preventing development of other less friendly bacteria. Most bacteria rather prefer a neutral or slightly alkaline environment, unlike yeasts, a preference capitalized in one process of making whole-wheat bread. A little added vinegar permits the yeast to do its work of gas making to open up the loaf while completely discouraging the offensive ropy-bread bacterium.

As chemical laborers on a factory scale bacteria have only recently been set to work. A notable example is the *chlostridium acetobutylicum,* employed to convert starch into butyl alcohol (for the cellulose lacquer industry), acetone, a valuable commercial solvent, and a few lesser products.

Molds as sources of antibiotics now hold the spotlight.

SOME LEADING ANTIBIOTICS

Penicillin, effective against	⎧ Pneumonia ⎨ Scarlet fever ⎬ Syphilis and gonorrhea ⎩ Mastoiditis, etc.
Streptomycin, " "	⎧ Tuberculosis (certain types) ⎨ Peritonitis ⎬ Whooping cough ⎩ Bubonic plague, etc.
Aureomycin, " "	⎧ Typhus fever and scrub fever ⎨ Typhoid and undulant fever ⎬ Amebic dysentery ⎩ Scarlet fever and shingles, etc.
Chloromycetin, " "	⎧ Typhoid and scrub fevers ⎨ Rocky Mountain fever ⎬ Spotted fever ⎩ Whooping cough, etc.
Terramycin, " "	⎧ Undulant fever and spotted fever ⎨ Blood poisoning ⎬ Whooping cough ⎩ Trench mouth, etc.

XXVII

CHAINING THE SUN

EVERYBODY KNOWS that solar radiation extends beyond the visible wave lengths, down into the longer infra-red or heat waves and up into the shorter or ultra-violet. But it has been shown that radio waves, heat waves, visible light, ultra-violet, X-rays, cosmic rays, are all parts of one tremendous band of radiation alike in velocity but differing in wave length. Calling visible light range one octave we can consider the entire range about 60 octaves. The cosmic rays are the shortest and the radio rays the longest in wave length.

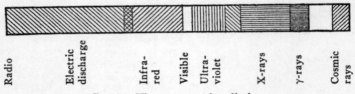

Radio — Electric discharge — Infra-red — Visible — Ultra-violet — X-rays — γ-rays — Cosmic rays

FIG. 71. The octaves of radiation.

Is radiation a wave motion in a mysterious "ether" filling all space or is light made up of beams of moving particles, little pockets of energy, called quanta? Experimental evidence supports both theories.

The wave theory and the corpuscular theory of light have each had their advocates. Now we are told that a beam of electrons behaves as if composed of a succession of very small waves. Interference effects (as with light waves) can be produced by beams of known particles. Consequently a particle of matter is either the center of a series of wavelets or a series of wavelets has the properties formerly attributed to a particle. Both energy and matter act as if they were composed of waves and as if they were composed of particles.

But at any rate we know that light does things, that our

energy came originally from the sun. The energy we unlock today by burning a lump of coal was locked up some millions of years ago in a tree fern by the marvelous action of green chlorophyll of the leaf in converting light energy into chemical energy. This green chlorophyll, $C_{55}H_{72}O_5N_4Mg$, a highly complicated magnesium compound, is the means of life on the earth, of most life at least. It is formed in plants only

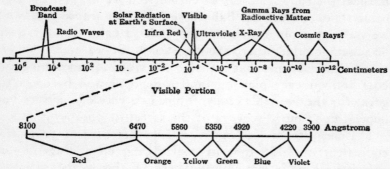

FIG. 72. The range of electromagnetic radiation. Courtesy Smithsonian Institution.

when the sun shines on them and then it aids, catalyzes, the reaction between carbon dioxide of the air and water of the plant sap.

$$6CO_2 + 5H_2O \rightarrow 6O_2 + C_6H_{10}O_5, \text{ starch.}$$

The beautiful economy of this reaction is something to admire, like any other masterpiece. Carbon dioxide in millions of tons is poured into the atmosphere by processes of fermentation, decay, combustion, breathing and would finally choke us but for the friendly aid of green plants and some help from shellfish in the ocean. Now you can guess where the oyster shell got part of its calcium carbonate. To afford good contact between air and chlorophyll the average leaf offers some 12,000,000 entrances, stomata, into its own interior. To use up the carbon dioxide given off by the average man in 24 hours some 60 square meters of green leaf surface are required.

Fortunately the green leaf turns loose into the air all the oxygen contained in the carbon dioxide and deposits in the tissues of the growing plant starch or sugar or cellulose. Consequently the energy obtained on eating or burning such plant material was the transformed solar energy that made our great reaction go. We call it "photosynthesis" and flatter Nature by trying to imitate her. Able research workers are trying to capture the secret of the chlorophyll so that we may harness the sun; set a vat of carbonated water, and the right catalyst, out in the hot Sahara sun with assurance that when we wake up from a pleasant nap under a palm tree there will be sugar or some other carbohydrate in the water.

What a dream—but it may come true! If our reserves of coal and oil ever play out and the population becomes too great for the available crops, future existence of our race may depend upon our discovery of the secret of photosynthesis.

"Energy from the sun pours on every acre of ground an equivalent of 1476 tons of coal during an average 90-day growing season in our Middle West. Of this wealth of power a crop of wheat yielding 50 bushels per acre, a very high yield, puts into the bin an energy equivalent of less than two-thirds of one ton of coal" (*H. A. Spoehr*).

This is an appalling waste of good solar energy and tempts us to reduce the green-leaf mechanism to a factory scale. There is hope and yet there are scientific skeptics who doubt it.

Lange has made a photoelectric cell from two layers of copper with a film of copper oxide in between. When light falls on one of the thin copper layers electrons are driven off, through the copper oxide to the other copper layer. The current of electricity is very small yet it is an encouraging start.

In Washington, D. C., the solar energy on a clear summer day at noon is 1.3 calories per square centimeter per minute. Even at a single calorie rate the solar energy on one acre equals 4,100 horse power. In April, 1936, Dr. Charles G. Abbot of the Smithsonian Institution in Washington exhibited an arrangement of mirror troughs heating a dark, high-boiling liquid (in glass tubes) which, flowing over water tubes, converted the water into steam for an engine.

The best previous steam-solar engine on a large scale was built in Egypt, 1913, by Schuman and Boys. The mirror surface was 0.3 acre and the efficiency, or fraction of total solar energy made useful, was only 4.5 per cent. So far such devices have cost more than the ordinary boiler and steam engine they sought to replace.

In late 1936, news came to us of an able chemist converting fully 10 per cent of solar energy directly into electricity. Longitudinal reflectors, moving with the sun by clock-mechanism, throw solar radiation directly on a series of small inexpensive converters. Fully 80 per cent of the total cost is credited to the mirrors of magnalium alloy.

Logical use of such devices is for irrigation pumps in dry, sunny regions or on isolated farms in sunnier areas where costs of power lines or coal or oil may be excessive.

The "Electric Eye," so useful in counting people who pass in the light, sacks that fall down a chute, cars that pass, or in automatically controlling mechanical movements, is merely a photoelectric cell. "The typical photoelectric cell," says Ives, "is a glass bulb (evacuated or containing a little inert gas) with one electrode, the cathode, usually a layer of alkali metal (rubidium) on the inner surface, with a wire leading out through the glass, and another electrode, the anode, a loop of wire, likewise carried out. Connect these two wires through a galvanometer and let light shine into the bulb; the galvanometer will show an electric current flowing. The current starts and stops instantaneously; it is proportional to the illumination." These photoelectrons, driven out of the metal layer by light, can be pushed around the circuit by an outside battery. The fact that the electric current varies with the intensity of the incident light makes the device useful.

An interesting suggestion for its use is as a burglar alarm. Any nocturnal prowler walking through, and interrupting an invisible beam of ultra-violet light shining on an electric eye device, would set off alarms. This item may seem trivial but there is real importance in the use of the photoelectrical cell for television and the talkies. Then, too, think of the intelligent electric eye that turns on more ventilating fans as the smoke or haze in a Hudson River tunnel increases. Passenger elevators can now be equipped so that they will not operate while anyone stands in the doorway. And why not turn your auto headlight directly on a phototube above the garage door and enjoy seeing the doors open automatically? Will you equip your house with thermostats to turn on the heat when it gets cold and "light-o-stats" to turn on the lights when it gets dark? The photoelectric cell is at its best when the bulb is filled with argon at 0.1 mm. pressure. For the talking pictures a beam of light passing through the sound tracks on the film hits a photoelectric cell with variations in light intensity which are reproduced through the amplifier and loud speaker as sound and speech.

When Daguerre, almost exactly a century ago, utilized the decomposition of silver iodide by sunlight,

$$2AgI \rightarrow I_2 + 2Ag,$$

followed by development of the latent image with fumes of mercury to trace a pattern of varying thickness of metallic silver on a plate, making the first photograph (a "daguerrotype"), he made it possible to tickle our vanity, to recreate history, to further education, entertain the millions, increase the revealing power of the telescope and to give medicine and surgery the X-ray. There are many chemical reactions caused by light, each one especially sensitive to a narrow band of the spectrum. Even the photographic film is more affected by some wave lengths of light than by others. However, by the aid of certain dyes that absorb the energy of the less actinic rays, the silver bromide may be sensitized to all the colors and a more accurate photograph be obtained. Such plates are termed "panchromatic."

In recent years it has been shown that the chemical change in the silver bromide started at certain sensitive spots and that if the purest gelatin was mixed with the silver salt in forming the film there was a great decrease in sensitivity. Search for the useful impurity in the grade of gelatin always used commercially showed the presence of traces of mustard oil which formed specks of silver sulfide, the active spots of

FIG. 73. A possible result of a great kodak company's discovery that minute traces of mustard oil in hide gelatin are essential to the proper sensitivity of photographic plates.

the film. A striking illustration of extreme sensitization is formed in a chemical related to the hemin of red blood corpuscles. Were this derivative formed in the blood a man would be dangerously light-struck by ordinary daylight.

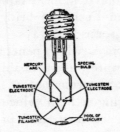

FIG. 74. The "Sunlight Lamp." Heat from the tungsten filament vaporizes enough mercury to form a mercury vapor arc, rich in ultra-violet light. The special glass lets out enough ultra-violet to give a light bath at three feet equal in medical effect to the noonday sun. (G. E. Co.)

As it is we must be careful in exposing ourselves to ultra-violet light, either from the tropical sun or the modern ultra-violet lamps. The right exposure creates vitamin D in the body, prevents rickets of the bones in children, but too much causes painful sunburn. Clear quartz is transparent to these short invisible light waves, while common glass cuts them off. Special glasses are now made, at an extra cost, for hospitals and sun-rooms. It is of passing interest to note that polished aluminum is the best reflector of incident ultra-violet.

As an amusing demonstration of the phosphorescence caused by ultra-violet rays striking certain substances, lecturers have turned a beam of this invisible light on an audience instructed to show its teeth, in the dark. All the natural teeth glowed with a ghostly light. Since different substances fluoresce under ultra-violet illumination with different colors, if at all, it is possible to use such beams in the dark to detect alterations in checks or in paintings or to identify marked currency.

Photographic plates are sensitive to ultra-violet rays (through quartz lenses, of course), but not to the longer infra-red unless sensitized by certain dyes. With such plates infra-red photographs have been taken of mountains 300 miles distant. Infra-red rays penetrate haze better than visible light.

The new sodium-vapor lamp with its yellow glow has spectacular possibilities, for it is said to be three or four times as efficient as the ordinary filament lamp of the same candle-power. The great San Francisco bridge is lighted by these sodium lamps, as are some highways.

Millikan's cosmic rays, which penetrate yards of lead and nearly half a mile of water, are probably made up of photons of light (which knock electrons out of matter) and of actual charged particles moving at high velocity.

Sterilizing lamps are now used in operating rooms of hospitals and in cold storage of foods. With its aid in killing moulds that would develop at a temperature suitable for rapid tenderizing of beef by enzymes present, tough meat may be made more valuable. For killing bacteria the most effective ultra-violet wave length seems to be 2537Å.

XXVIII

WINDOWS TOWARD HEAVEN

JUST AS Hebrew captives in ancient Babylon "kept their windows open toward Jerusalem" so, in the broader sense, man has always wanted windows through which he might look toward Heaven.

Yet mere openings in the wall without some sort of transparent protection let in the blustery wind, the biting cold, the soaking rain. Possibly animal skins, scraped thin, were better than nothing and it may well be that some luxurious Cæsar enjoyed window glazing in the form of thin sheets of marble made translucent with oils.

Then, some 5,000 years ago came glass, discovered no doubt by the fortuitous use of chunks of limestone and natural soda in protecting some campfire on a sand beach. Given sand, lime, soda, and sufficient heat anybody can make crude glass. To be sure the simple art finally became a science, but it must have had its origin in accident. Egypt fostered the ancient art and gave it color, as we can see in Oriental museums. The glass bottles that caught the royal tears of some Pharaoh's daughter have been preserved, with their lovely iridescence increasing with each passing century.

Now glass windows protect us from adverse climate while permitting us to enjoy sky, land, and sea. If this were all, we could say that glass has greatly enriched life, but there is much more to be told. It is through great plate glass windows that the strolling world enjoys the tempting merchandise of shops and by strong glass windows that the motorist is given the comforts of a closed car. Nor is it daylight alone that we capture with glass for house and greenhouse. Without glass there would have been no lamp chimney for the oil-burning days nor electric lamp bulbs to the number of nearly 500,-

000,000 in the United States. And what about jars for preserved foods and bottles for milk, medicines and drinks?

Yes, in all probability, you will agree that glass has most profoundly affected the human race when shaped into the lenses of the telescope, the microscope, the camera, and the eyeglass. It is only three hundred years from the birth of Leeuwenhoek, who made the first effective microscope. Its magnifying power was not great and not until after Abbé's work, about fifty years ago, was it possible to obtain clear magnification of 1000 diameters (equal to 1,000,000 areas).

FIG. 75. It was a long way from flaming torch to tungsten lamp.

When Leeuwenhoek in 1675 contrived a crude microscope and saw bacteria and protozoa in water ("wee beasties") he gave the world knowledge of greater importance than the rise and fall of empires—yet the world yawned and disregarded his discoveries for near two centuries.

The climax of this effort to peer into the structure of the infinitely small has just been reached. Lucas, himself a man of defective vision, has taught the world how to use the already-invented ultra-violet microscope operating with those invisible rays, the ultra-violet, and has increased useful magnification up to 6,000 diameters. However, a transparent quartz lens takes the place of a glass lens, for common glass is opaque to ultra-violet. The invisible light used is made visible by means of a fluorescent screen which becomes luminous under illumination by the ultra-violet. Though the eye is not sensitive to these rays just shorter than the violet, the photographic plate accurately records their presence. Lucas has opened up alluring new fields in the study of alloys, of cells, of bacteria, and made it possible to deal optically with dimensions up to (or down to) one millionth of an inch.

As we have said before, without the microscope there could be no scientific study of bacteria, no complete understanding of disease. The electron microscope, using streams of electrons instead of light, gives a magnification of 30,000 diameters.

The telescope, extending man's vision outward, is, like the microscope, rapidly pushing back horizons. A few years ago a 69-inch reflecting glass mirror for a telescope was completed after six years of effort. Such a mass of glass weighing nearly two tons had to be cooled with painful patience through many months, to prevent the development of strains. Too-rapid polishing distorts glass by the heat evolved.

The great 200-inch glass reflector for a giant telescope on Mount Palomar weighs 20 tons (glass mirror alone). A new glass had to be invented and a new reflecting surface (sputtered aluminum) capable of utilizing the ultra-violet radiation from distant stars. Such a telescope (aided by the camera) will ultimately reveal 1,500,000,000 stars, three times former possibility. The safe cooling of this glass disk took about a year and the grinding and polishing required three years. The cost of the telescope amounted to millions of dollars.

Glass, as you may know, is a mixture of silicates, usually of sodium and calcium, yet lead is substituted for part of the calcium in certain special varieties. Borax replaces a portion of the sand in the pyrex or resistant type of borosilicate glass so much used now in chemical laboratories and in kitchens. It expands and contracts so little with sudden changes in temperature that baking dishes are made of it. Fortunately cheaper borax from California came along just in time for this new development.

The green color of cheap glass is due to iron impurities, which form ferrous silicate. The traditional method of curing this fault was by oxidation to the almost colorless ferric silicate through addition of manganese dioxide. Selenium, cousin to sulfur, has been substituted with effective production of clear glass. With an excess, ruby glass is produced, rivalling the red glass made by the aid of a trace of gold. All the blue glass you ever saw was colored with cobalt compounds. To such tricks do we owe the magnificent stained glass windows of Notre Dame in Paris—to them and to the softening effects of time.

The blowing of glass into cylinders or other shapes was a hand-to-mouth art until very recent years. Now a ring, dipped into a fiery pool, is slowly raised until a tower of red hot glass forty feet high and a few feet in diameter grows upward in the murky darkness of the mill. Or a bar is dipped into molten glass and drawn out, followed by a broad ribbon of the melt, cooling enough to be run through rolls and brought to the proper thickness. The cylinder first described can be cut and flattened to a sheet suitable for window glass.

Heavy plate glass windows, however, must be cast, cooled, ground, and polished. Naturally they are not cheap. A single Owens bottle-blowing machine does the work of fifty men, making 10,000 bottles per hour. We need such machines, to make the 500,000,000 milk bottles demanded every year in this country, and the 20,000,000,000 of other bottles and jars. In a good year the products of the American glass industry are worth more than $1,000,000,000.

Manufacturers predict an age of glass with new applications now only talked of. Triplex or laminated glass for use as non-shattering windows of motor cars is saving lives and making money—an excellent combination. The cellulose acetate or vinylite plastic sheet in the middle, glued powerfully to two sheets of glass, holds all broken fragments.

Special glasses, reasonably permeable to the ultra-violet rays of sunlight, are now ready for your sun porch. With common glass you get warmth and good cheer but no health-giving qualities through the windows of your solarium. It is conceivable that a glass opaque to infra-red heat rays may be invented for use in the tropics.

Finally note that "water glass" is not a glass at all but a single silicate, sodium silicate, in fact. In viscous water solutions it is the cheapest adhesive known, used in enormous quantities in making cardboard boxes.

XXIX

THE CHEMIST IN
CRIME DETECTION

IN FICTION and in fact we generally look for the brains behind the crime and then we hire trained intelligence to catch and convict the criminals. Of course the physician is authority on disease, time of death, nature of wounds, poisoning, but the fingerprint expert is there almost as soon. The ballistic expert does wonders in "finger-printing" bullets (if any) through his microscopic study of the trifling and slight imperfections in the gun barrel possibly used or owned by the suspect. J. H. Matthews tells of the conviction of a brute who used a knife on some willows in preparing a hiding place. Unfortunately for the criminal he kept the knife. By comparison of photographs (enlarged) of the characteristic parallel markings left on fresh cuttings with this knife and those at the scene of the crime the jury was convinced that only this particular knife could have made the original cuttings.

Handwriting experts are needed in cases of forgery or threatening letters, and experts in any field may be asked about the possibilities. The mass of accumulated evidence and clues must be used by police, prosecutor or "G" men with horse sense, practical psychology, patience, courage and resourcefulness.

Back of this scene stands the chemist, ready and able to serve, frequently called in. The public thinks of his share as mere analysis of suspected food or stomach for poison or of stains on clothing. This and much more is his function. On the stage or screen the master mind (chemical, we hope) exclaims "Ha! A mote—or mite—of dust from the suspect's coat sleeve proves to be rare monozite sand from Ceylon because of its definite thorium content. And the murdered man was a famous scientist engaged in research on the helium gas known to be imprisoned in such sand."

It is true that arsenic, phenol (carbolic acid), the alkaloids and many other poisons possibly retained in stomach, liver or other organs of the body are revealed only by chemical analysis (aided by symptoms). A test for carbon monoxide in the blood may decide between accidental death (or suicide) in the garage and murder.

Stains may be examined with the microscope but the chemist, of course, is asked to reveal their composition. If rusty in appearance they may be iron oxide rust or blood. Iron is easily recognized and blood solution shows definite light absorption bands when viewed with a spectroscope. Blood haemoglobin yields a blue color on contact with benzidine and hydrogen peroxide but this test is merely preliminary. Detection of the difference between human blood and animal blood is not so simple. Antisera are now obtainable which give a peculiar precipitate with human blood extracts —under carefully controlled conditions.

In an Egyptian murder case the suspect denied being near the scene of the crime, the seashore, yet water washings of his clothing showed plenty of common salt from the ocean spray. Stains from bomb outrages sometimes reveal yellow picric acid while powder stains in general leave their chemical mark. A sharper accused of dissolving a little gold from coins with aqua regia (mixture of nitric and hydrochloric acids) was given a thorough hand-washing. The presence of both chlorides and nitrates convicted him. Perspiration contains common salt (sodium chloride) but not nitrates.

No clever detective would overlook the dust on clothing, in pockets or pants cuffs and if super-clever he would look for invisible stains. Here the tool of fluorescence and fluorescence photography comes in. Many substances, colorless in ordinary light, give off visible light of characteristic colors under ultraviolet radiation, readily observed in a dark room or recorded on a photographic plate. By this tool the presence of suspected chemicals on clothing, documents or paintings has been revealed. Alterations on a check will show up clearly under ultra-violet light, for the surface finish is marred. Fraudulent "old masters" suffer under examination by ultra-violet or infra-red light due to the knowledge of variations in paint pigments available in different centuries. Infra-red photography is possible now, thanks to dyes that sensitize the plate to this wave length of light (just a little longer than the visible waves).

Inks, dyes, oils, brands of gasoline, fragments of metal, even putty, are part of the extensive repertoire of the crime chemist. The very efficient New York State Crime Laboratory (which should be widely imitated) convicted a safeblower because he left a can of putty behind. He used the putty to seal up the safe in a Waterford theater preparatory to placing a nitroglycerine charge and got some putty under his fingernails. Analysis revealed the same composition and consistency for these fingernail scrapings and the putty found at the scene of the crime. A jury convicted him in record time.

Around Great Bear Lake, on Canada's Arctic Circle, they detect new radium ore deposits by the audible clicks of the Geiger counter, sensitive to electrons. This is no crime but the same tool might be used to trace stolen radium.

XXX

THE FARM AS A
FACTORY

TIMES HAVE certainly changed on the farm and they will continue to change. Only a century ago seven out of every ten workers in this country lived on farms but now only two out of ten men earn their living directly from the soil. We are not fasting, at least not many millions of us; in fact we are demanding a greater variety of food while exporting a large tonnage.

The trouble is, if you can call it trouble, that the farming industry, like all manufacturing, has been mechanized and fewer men are needed to produce more food. Adjustment to this change has caused some hardship but that is the usual price for swift changes in our economic life.

After all, the farm has become a factory requiring intelligent management like all other factories.

Raw Materials	Soil	Products	Grains	Eggs
	Water		Grass and hay	Fruits
	Fertilizers		Beef	Vegetables
	Air		Pork	Cotton
			Poultry	Sugar
			Mutton and wool	Lumber
			Milk and butter	Fats

The farm-manufacturer is no exception to the rule that he must produce the utmost possible for a given amount of work, for the capital invested, for a given cost of raw materials, and he must see that the quality of product is high. Like any business man he is obliged to study markets and to vary production accordingly. To this end the farmer is building good roads to market and using power machinery to replace animal labor. Much of the drudgery of earlier farm life is gone, along with the former isolation and lack of conveniences. Now 95 per cent of the farms in the United States are electrified with the resulting conveniences of much labor-saving machinery.

Four million farm tractors now do the work of many million horses. In the corn belt one man on a tractor can plow 32 acres in a day and do it well. It is rumored that the Russian Soviet is sowing wheat by airplane and, for that matter, it is known that we dust poisons on cottonfield, forest, and mosquito swamp with the aid of the plane. The gasoline engine and the

FIG. 76. Plowing was difficult in ancient Egypt.

electric motor cut costs and add comfort. The largest "combine" cuts and threshes over forty acres of wheat in a day using only two men who, a century ago, could not have accomplished the task in three months.

Such mechanization of the American farm has already reduced the farm population because fewer farmers can now produce more food.

Several years ago we exported to China rice produced by machine methods with the highest-priced agricultural labor in the world and competed successfully with rice grown in the Orient with hand labor at fifteen cents a day. In this and in other fields it is engineering that enables our farmer to compete in world markets. The U. S. Department of Agriculture published a comparison of the use of power in farming in various countries. It is worth a glance, for it indicates that the larger farms in the prairie areas of the West can profit-

FOOTNOTE. Hybrid corn has added $1,000,000,000 yearly to the value of our corn crop while the soybean crop is worth $800,000,000.

Use of 22,000,000 tons of fertilizer, great amounts of weed killers and insect poisons, plus abundant farm machinery, improved stock feed and treatment of animal diseases have added enormously to the productivity of our farms.

ably use more power machines than are economical in the smaller and more hilly farms of the East.

Any system of permanent agriculture requires the return to the soil of some of the elements removed by crops. The three elements to which special attention must be given are nitrogen, phosphorus, and potassium (N, P, and K), so all complete fertilizers contain their compounds in available form. Fertilizer in the form of manure or crop refuse has always been used but not until 1830–1840 were the first "commercial fertilizers," Peruvian guano or bird refuse, and Chile saltpeter, introduced into Europe. In 1860 the great chemist Liebig announced the value of potassium salts or "potash" as plant food; ammonium sulfate was added to the list of fertilizers in 1875, and this was followed in 1888 by the discovery of phosphate rock in Florida. Earlier chapters in this book have told the story of the conquest of the air by the chemist, the transformation of "free" nitrogen into compounds available as plant food.

A proof of the value of government effort is found in the deep potash deposits of Texas and New Mexico, somewhat similar to the dominating Stassfurt deposits of Germany. Drillings showed much promise and mines are in full operation. Distance from markets will handicap this development as it does the industry at Searles Lake, California. However, in 1956, our United States production of potassium salts reached 1,750,000 tons, estimated as K_2O or "potash," making us independent of German and French potash. In case of another war and potash shortage the Searles Lake company and the New Mexico field can multiply production to meet all our needs.

Phosphates need not trouble this country, for only France and the United States possess adequate deposits of phosphate rock. Russia is proposing to make soluble phosphate or "superphosphate" from the apatite ore found on the shores of the White Sea.

It is to be expected that European countries with crowded populations must use more fertilizers per acre than we do and these earlier figures confirm this: Holland, 367 pounds per acre; Germany, 72; Japan, 56; France, 35; Italy, 21; and the United States, 8. We must produce *more crops per man* while Europe finds it best economy, with cheaper labor and more expensive land, to produce more per acre.

The scientific farmer is learning how to improve his food factory and how to avoid troubles and pests, from the agricultural research work carried on by the state and national governments. They teach him to add a few pounds per acre of manganese salts to an unproductive land in Florida in order to secure bumper crops of tomatoes or in another district to add a few pounds of magnesium compounds to improve the yield of tobacco. Where the soil contained too much lime, plants needing iron have become yellow, anemic, due to the action of the lime in binding iron into an insoluble form. Use of fertilizers making the soil less basic or even slightly acid has sometimes cured this anemia. Now Carr at Purdue informs us that different types of soils show marked differences in the ash of the crops. "Strawberries grown on a certain clay soil remained firm and marketable four days longer than the same variety grown on a near-by loam soil. Wheat from a certain silt soil contained 20 per cent more ash, produced a larger loaf of bread than the same variety grown on a productive loam soil in the same locality."

It seems rather far-fetched to drag in the surgeons' tools as aids to farming yet it is now proposed to use certain anesthetics to shorten the dormant or rest period of tree seedings, potatoes and other plants where time of production is an important factor.

A well-balanced ration for stock is quite common on the modern farm—carried to the point of adding cod liver oil to chicken feed, antibiotics to stock feed, for growth and general vigor. The latest proposal with vitamin foods comes from Steenbock and his associates at the University of Wisconsin. They would have all cows fed daily with a few ounces of yeast that had been irradiated with ultra-violet light. The plain, and vitally important, fact is that milk does not contain enough vitamin D to prevent rickets in children. Cod liver oil prevents rickets in man but when fed to cows does not confer much additional vitamin D potency on the milk. A little irradiated yeast in the cows' ration can readily increase several-fold the anti-rachitic property of ordinary milk, or the milk can be irradiated.

Labor-saving use of dynamite on the farm is not new but it is good business when it comes to clearing land of stumps and large rocks, or ditching extensive swamps, or breaking the hardpan where young fruit trees are to be planted.

No manufacturer has so many enemies as the farmer. Insects, as we related in a previous chapter, cause a national loss of $4,000,000,000 while plant diseases account for as much more. In the fierce battle for existence the farmer uses more than 20,000,000 pounds each of the arsenates of lead and calcium as ammunition. Eternal vigilance is the price of success.

New crops are being considered. Millions of acres of the Manchurian soy bean are planted, enriching the soil as do all legumes, and yielding a generous crop of a fatty bean destined to become one of the greatest human foods. A large acreage in Florida has been planted with tung oil trees with a view to supplying our paint market with the $23,000,000 one time paid to China for this quick-drying oil.

Our Department of Agriculture has taught the world how to grow the tubers of the Jerusalem artichoke and how to make from these tubers levulose, nearly twice as sweet as cane sugar, but no farm-factory combination takes advantage of this great research given to the public. From sixteen tons per acre 400 gallons of alcohol could be made.

We have just discovered how to obtain from ramie grass (which could be grown in the South) longer and stronger fibers than those now made from cotton, flax, or hemp. Will we benefit from this discovery?

The United States paper pulp industry has been driven to Canada for lack of raw material. We should treat the forest as a crop and supply the pulpwood. Charles Herty, down in Georgia, has proved with a small factory, that good white paper and rayon can be made from young "slash pine" —another quickly-grown crop. Farm and forest go together. The South has 100,000,000 acres of unproductive, cut-over timber land that should be cropped with young pines, cut after ten or fifteen years before increasing content of resin makes paper making too difficult.

Cellulose, the greatest crop in the world, makes up half the weight of dry wood, all the weight of cotton, and the fiber of many plants, even the bamboo. It should be considered as so much raw material for factory transformation into useful chemicals such as sugars, or into paper, artificial wood, and the like.

A most intelligent attack on farm wastes is now being made. Out of 175,000,000 tons of cornstalks and 20,000,000 tons of corncobs something could be made, if the high cost of collecting the material can be reduced. As a matter of fact furfural, used as a solvent in the manufacture of plastics, is now made from oat hulls, and could be made from corncobs.

Cottonseed was once a nuisance but now its annual value as a source of cotton linters, oil, and meal exceeds $400,-000,000. It may well be that the wood distillation industry producing adsorbent charcoal, acetone, acetic acid, tar and gas will change to corncobs and similar farm wastes as raw material. Xylose, the new sugar waiting for a use, is made from cottonseed bran but could be made from our 100,000 tons of peanut shells.

A mixture of cornstalks and sewage can be fermented to yield large volumes of good fuel gas. Perhaps the factory-farm of the future will obtain light, heat, and power from this source.

With all this improvement in farm efficiency our Secretary of Agriculture warns us that we must also carry on more rural social research to guarantee that farming shall become a better "way of living."

Southern farmers now face a problem, for the cotton-picking machine, more than ready, is really a success. Three fourths of the workers in cotton fields may need to find other work. This machine combs the cotton from the plant by adhesion of the fiber to smooth, moistened metal rods.

The Farm Chemurgic conferences have directed national attention to the farm as a factory. It was urged that 10 per cent grain alcohol be mixed in gasoline. However, ordinary 95 per cent alcohol does not mix with gasoline, hence the necessity of preparing the more expensive 99.5 per cent liquid.

Development of the soybean industry was another feature of these conferences, quite in line with Henry Ford's enthusiasm for that cause. Here the chemist and the farmer must cooperate.

And now to complicate the situation "dirtless farming" is being demonstrated by Gericke at the University of California. Enormous crops of potatoes, tomatoes and other vegetables are grown in tanks of water containing the proper fertilizer chemicals. The seeds are sown in a mulch of moss or excelsior resting on a wire netting near the surface of the water. With the aid of a heating coil tobacco plants 22 feet high were grown while tomatoes were harvested from stepladders. With such gardens the barren island of Guam in the Pacific might well grow fresh vegetables for staff and visitors when it becomes important as a naval or airways base.

The corn and wheat farmer in 1942 insisted on making a good share of the butadiene required for the chief synthetic rubber, using the steps: starch→alcohol—butadiene→rubber. He must compete with the petroleum refinery and with the molasses→alcohol→butadiene process.

Waxy corn is a new farm crop launched on a commercial scale by Iowa State College scientists in 1943. These enterprising men crossed Chinese popcorn with American hybrid corn to produce a corn containing starch of the same peculiar qualities as tapioca starch. The economic importance of this development is evident when you learn that in 1941 we imported 352,000,000 pounds of tapioca, mainly for the manufacture of adhesives.

XXXI

WHAT TRANSPORTA-TION OWES TO THE CHEMIST

WHEN TRANSPORTATION depended mainly upon sailing vessels, camels, pack horses, and the Chinese wheelbarrow, the services of the chemist were not much in demand.

The Roman emperors bound distant provinces to the capitol by great military roads—but failed to invent swift vehicles to utilize these arteries of empire. Gaul was bound to Rome by 13,000 miles of improved roads.

Henry Vogt Machine Company.

FIG. 77. Freight transportation in the Orient.

With the invention of the steam engine and the coming of steamship and locomotive the world tasted the possibilities of speed and demanded more. The chemist was called in to make more and better steels for trains and rails. Every wreck due to a broken rail was a challenge to the steel maker, met with almost unbelievable improvement in quality. Even the X-ray and the radium beam are called in to discover flaws in rails.

Steamships demanded oil fuel—and got it. As a consequence the cruising range of navies is greatly lengthened, their speed increased, and working conditions of firemen improved. When petroleum is exhausted the chemist will be asked to develop other convenient liquid fuels. He has already anticipated the demand and will be prepared long in advance.

But the automobile is the special protégé of the chemist in spite of contrary claims from physicist and engineer. Without the modern alloy steels built to stand brutal strains and stresses, the passenger auto would be a lumbering truck. The introduction of chromium or manganese or vanadium or any of several other elements into steel met these exacting demands for toughness, hardness, and resistance to continued vibration. To this list of automobile aids had to be added

The First Wheel

The Wheel, Studebaker Co.

Fig. 78. The evolution of transportation (six stages).

chromium plating, aluminum or magnesium alloys to lighten the car, and copper for electrical parts.

Without oil refining there would have been no car at all for the internal combustion engine demands rather special liquid fuels. Our 60,000,000 cars require 30,000,000,000 gallons of gasoline annually, forcing the chemist to crack or hydrogenate less valuable distillates in order to create enough acceptable motor fuel. If the diesel engine becomes common in auto trucks and buses a cruder oil can be utilized. The day may come when fats will be produced as motor fuel or when coal dust will be exploded in the cylinder with effective results. Rest assured, the automobile will never lack for fuel.

In 1895 on Thanksgiving Day the first auto race in America was run. A Duryea horseless buggy won at the mad speed of nine miles per hour. We have come a long way since then.

To say that the auto waited for a powerful but light framework and a suitable fuel is not enough. How would you enjoy riding a mile a minute on hard steel tires? The old-

FIG. 79.

fashioned horse and buggy never got up the speed necessary to jar liver and spine to limit of endurance. A modern car equipped with those buggy wheels would surely make speed laws unnecessary.

So rubber joins the group of essentials to the automotive industry and yet we do not produce it in our own country. It seems possible that the guayule plant of the dry Southwest, the goldenrod, the intisny plant from Madagascar, may provide some natural rubber.

FIG. 80.

The new synthetic rubber, "neoprene," announced early in 1932 by the duPont Company, is made from limestone, coke, and common salt, by a very difficult process based upon Nieuwland's earlier work. Acetylene is one of the intermediates. However we are now making over 1,000,000 tons yearly of GR-S, the best synthetic rubber for all except some heavy-duty tires.

The first cars were elaborately and expensively finished with several coats of paint but later coats of nitrocellulose lacquers were quickly sprayed on. To prepare the metal for

"Duco" or similar finishes, a spray of glyptal resin is applied and baked on as a base. A neat bit of chemistry was involved in the conversion of the naphthalene of moth balls, and glycerine, into "glyptal." Now better lacquers are available.

It is needless to remind you that the non-shattering window with its two sheets of glass powerfully glued to a middle sheet of cellulose acetate or vinylite is now almost as essential to the motorist's happiness as the splendid grades of lubricant carefully prepared for him by the petroleum chemist.

The airplane, like the auto, had to wait for invention of a light and effective internal combustion engine. The necessity for weight-saving alloys was even greater, however, and none

FIG. 81.

but the best gasoline and lubricant was to be tolerated. Now it is routine to operate regular airline service at a few hundred miles per hour.

The giant dirigible airships were out of the question without a light and powerful aluminum alloy such as duralumin for framework, and hydrogen or helium gases for buoyancy.

Just as heavy, fast-flying trains require perfect rails, so do swift autos depend upon smooth and broad highways of cement or tar-surfaced rock. In a decade the United States spent ten billions of dollars on road construction, and considered the resulting annihilation of distance well worth the stupendous cost.

Portland cement, covering the country with a great network of roads and walks, is not made at Portland. Joseph Aspdin, the Englishman who rediscovered the secret of making it about a century ago, thought it resembled stone quarried from the Isle of Portland. Rediscovered is the right word, for the ancient Romans made a similar product, Puzzolan cement, by burning together lime and volcanic ashes. We can make it by grinding and roasting a mixture of blast furnace slag and lime, but most of our annual production of 350,-000,000 barrels is prepared from limestone and clay. Mere mixing is not enough—the ground material is fed into a gigantic rotating tube, nine feet in diameter and three hundred feet long, so that the charge slowly approaches the roaring thirty-foot flame of burning coal dust. In this hot zone the dirt almost fuses, forms little hard clinkers. These are ground so fine that four fifths of the powder will pass through a sieve with 40,000 holes per square inch. You must

FIG. 82.

keep this stuff out of the rain for it is a "hydraulic cement" like plaster of Paris, chemically reacting with water to form a hard rock. Your cement road is prepared by mixing the dry cement with about six times as much sand and gravel—and the necessary water. The final hardened product is termed "concrete."

The Hoover Dam would not have been built but for the discovery of the Portland cement process. This mammoth structure, containing 4,400,000 cubic yards of concrete, developed so much heat from reactions of setting that it was necessary to incorporate 750 miles of cooling pipe as the mass grew in height. Cold water circulated through the pipes but finally they were filled with concrete paste. Without this precaution temperatures above normal would have continued for two centuries, it was estimated, and dangerous shrinkage cracks would have developed.

Concrete roads, costing as much as $100,000 per mile, are too expensive for all highway purposes. Secondary feeders to main arteries must be made of crushed rock surfaced with sand and asphalt (possibly costing $30,000 per mile) or even of sand or clay given successive oiling, scarifying, and packing treatments.

Transportation in the future will be fiercely competitive, with speed, comfort, cost and safety carefully weighed. The railways are offering us air-conditioned cars filled with air that has been washed free of dusts, cooled and brought to the most comfortable degree of humidity. On stifling hot days such an atmosphere is rather alluring.

Fig. 83.

Pressurized planes for high altitude flying are now common. The attraction of speed and comfort gave the passenger plane such an advantage over travel by rail that the competition is severe.

More competition by buses causes another headache for rail executives. The freight truck cuts into rail revenues, exasperating rail owners who complain that trucks and buses do not have to build their roads.

The last straw is government maintenance of river highways for barges, carrying enormous quantities of freight. And yet it is healthy competition that spurs industry to greater efforts, lowered costs, improved efficiency.

Freight in the form of oil and gas is already sent by pipeline, as is mail within the limits of Paris. We may see powdered coal or coal dust in oil—perhaps in water—pumped hundreds of miles through iron tubes.

Some non-skid surface for roads, or tires, will, it is hoped, be developed before long. The demand for speed is leading now, but later the public will make safety a first consideration.

Great changes in transportation of people and freight will take place, but it scarcely seems possible to exceed in the next century the progress of the past century. Freight in England about 1800, cost twenty-seven cents per ton-mile, a rate that today would ruin their steel and coal industries.

FIG. 84. The farm was always far from markets in muddy weather.

Kaempffert calls our attention to a Frenchman's account of a journey from Philadelphia to Baltimore in 1788.

"From thence (Havre de Grace) to Baltimore are reckoned sixty miles. The road in general is frightful; it is over a clay soil full of deep ruts always in the midst of forests frequently obstructed by trees overset by the wind, which obliged us to seek a new passage through the woods. I can not conceive why the stage does not often overset. Both the drivers and their horses discover great skill and dexterity, being accustomed to these roads."

How potent is modern transportation in acquainting men of far-separated states; in bringing about better understanding between peoples; in adding to the possibilities of culture by travel! How it improves our health by bringing to the table a greater variety of fruits and vegetables; facilitates business; extends suburban areas; and unites farm and city!

XXXII

MINERALS AND
WORLD POWER

Up to the time of the industrial revolution a little more than a century ago the industrial and military powers of nations were determined more by population, agricultural resources and forests than by possession of mineral wealth. To be sure, guns and swords were of metal but the tonnage of steel or bronze required was relatively small. Ships sturdily built of old English oak ruled the seas while wooden coaches rolled and lurched along the highways.

With the arrival of the steam engine, the railway, the steel ship, the dynamo and motor, the automobile, control of minerals became essential to political and industrial power. For proof of this contention, glance at the following chart.

Energy sources $\begin{cases} \text{Coal} \\ \text{Oil} \\ \text{Oil shale} \end{cases}$

Metals for
dynamo, motor, $\begin{cases} \text{Copper} \\ \text{Iron} \\ \text{Aluminum} \end{cases}$
and transmission

Fertilizer
minerals $\begin{cases} \text{Phosphates} \\ \text{Potash} \end{cases}$

Metals
of
Mars
$\begin{cases} \text{Iron} \begin{cases} \text{Rifles, cannon, tanks} \\ \text{Shells, torpedoes} \\ \text{Ships} \end{cases} \\ \text{and} \\ \text{Steel} \\ \text{Aluminum} \begin{cases} \text{Aircraft} \end{cases} \\ \text{Copper and Zinc} \begin{cases} \text{Brass shells} \end{cases} \\ \text{Lead} \begin{cases} \text{Bullets} \\ \text{Storage batteries} \end{cases} \\ \text{Vanadium, nickel, chromium, tungsten} \begin{cases} \text{Alloy steels} \end{cases} \\ \text{Mercury} \begin{cases} \text{Detonating caps for shells} \end{cases} \end{cases}$

Industry in general
- Iron and Steel
  - Railway equipment
  - Automobiles
  - Buildings
  - Bridges
  - Ships
  - Machinery in general
- Copper
  - Electrical industry
  - Brass and bronze
  - Printing arts
  - Buildings
- Zinc
  - Brass
  - Pigment for paints and filler for tires
  - Galvanized iron
- Lead
  - Pigments for paints
  - Plumbing
  - Storage batteries
  - Type metal
  - Bearing metal
  - Solders
- Aluminum
  - Aircraft
  - Automobiles
  - Buildings
  - Furniture
  - Cooking utensils
  - Paint
  - Light, strong alloys
- Tin
  - Tin-plated steel
  - Bronze
- Nickel
  - Electric cable covering
  - Alloy steels
  - Plating
  - Monel metal
  - Electric resistance wire ("Nichrome")
- Gold
  - Coins
  - Jewelry
- Silver
  - Photography
  - Mirrors
  - Coins
- Platinum
  - Catalyst
  - Dentistry
  - Jewelry
  - Scientific uses
- Tungsten
  - Lamp filaments
  - High speed steels

Manganese
- Hard steels

Chromium
- Hard steels
- Rustless steels
- Plating

Vanadium
- Tough steels
- Catalysts

Magnesium
- Light alloys
- Star shells

Mercury
- Medicines
- Poisons
- Scientific instruments

The rapid depletion of these mineral resources in recent years is most alarming yet, deceived by present overproduction, the public remains unconcerned. Apparently it is up to the scientist, self-appointed as prophet and protector, to anticipate and avert a world-wide calamity.

Since 1900 the world consumption of mineral resources has exceeded that of all previous ages. Obviously such a prodigal spending of limited mineral wealth can not continue indefinitely. It is not enough to shrug shoulders and say,

FIG. 85. Crude metallurgy in ancient Egypt.

"After us the deluge." We must waste less in mining, recover more "scrap metal," and invent substitutes.

In a single year (1929) the United States used twice as much copper as the world produced up to 1800 and more zinc than all countries mined from 1800 to 1850. During the eight years prior to 1930 the world used more oil than in all the earlier years. Consequently we are actively searching for new sources of these metals and for new oil fields.

RELATIVE ABUNDANCE OF METALS
(with Zn = 1)

Aluminum	80,000	Copper	20
Iron	50,000	Cobalt	10
Titanium	4,000	Tin	5
Manganese	800	Lead	1
Chromium	400	Zinc	1
Nickel	200		

As Leith points out in his thrilling book, "World Minerals and World Politics," the greater part of these mineral foun-

dations of empire belong to countries bordering upon the
North Atlantic and for that reason the world must continue
to be dominated by the nations of this region. It is, therefore,
a matter for congratulation by us and envy by others that 40
per cent of the world's mineral resources are found in the
United States. Great Britain with Canada comes next in rank
and, if Australia, along with South Africa as parts of the
British Empire are included, the great commonwealth of
Dominions will nearly equal the United States in mineral resources. Only 15 or 20 per cent is left to be scrambled for
by all other nations.

The world was long ruled from the shores of the Mediterranean but that leadership is not likely to return, in the
face of the convincing statistics just given. France has potash,
coal, iron, and aluminum ores and in Tunis, Algiers, and
Morocco controls great iron ore beds, and phosphate deposits
equal to our own. Italy lacks coal and most of the important
minerals although well endowed with sulfur, aluminum ores,
and mercury, and possible potassium salt resources. Spain for
ages past has supplied civilization with a portion of the
needed copper, lead, silver, and mercury but her mineral
production is modest in comparison with present world needs.

The French position, if the island of New Caledonia with
its chromium and nickel as well as Madagascar with its
graphite are included, is very strong, far ahead of Germany.
Germany once lost much of her coal, iron, and potash to
neighboring states and is now in a very difficult position in
attempting to regain her former mighty seat in the circle of
dominant nations.

Russia with Siberia has vast reserves of coal, iron, oil,
salt, manganese, phosphates, probably much chromium,
copper, gold, and potash, and certainly the greater supply of
the world's platinum.

India and China are often said to be rich in minerals but
as a matter of fact neither is in a leading position in this respect. India produces one third of the world's manganese,
so important to steel making, and owns a good supply of

excellent iron ore and some petroleum and gold. She lacks the coal necessary for utilization of her iron ore. China leads all in production of tungsten and antimony (important in making type metal and lead storage battery plates) but her iron, coal, and gold are minor in present importance. The coal is of excellent quality. No doubt other mineral resources will later be discovered in China and in Siberia.

Japan, poorly endowed with minerals, naturally desires the coal and iron of Manchuria even though the iron ore is of low grade. From the viewpoint of Eastern politics it is worth noting that there are large deposits of iron ores in the Philippines and the islands of Indonesia. Diplomats may well be concerned with the recent discovery of the world's largest chromium ore deposit in the Philippines. And of course we all know that most of the world's tin comes from the East Indies and the Malay States.

Even with Manchuria, Japan can produce only a tenth of the iron her industries devour, a fraction of the cotton, less than 8 per cent of the oil, a tiny bit of the rubber, very little of the tin, lead or wool.

Africa is important, but not dominant, with mineral wealth. Iron ores of Morocco, phosphates of Algiers, Tunis, and Morocco, oil of Egypt, copper of Rhodesia and of the Belgian Congo, tin of Nigeria, gold and diamonds of South Africa, chromium of Rhodesia, manganese in the Gold Coast and Egypt, cadmium of the Belgian Congo, platinum and asbestos of South Africa, and graphite of Madagascar make an impressive total, but only in South Africa is there the proper combination for independent industrial power.

South America, too, lacks essential balance of minerals, lacks coal especially. Iron is abundant in Brazil and Chile, oil in Venezuela, Peru, Ecuador and Colombia, copper in Chile, aluminum ore of the best quality in British and Dutch Guiana, manganese in Brazil, platinum in Colombia, tin in Bolivia and vanadium in Peru.

Mexico has little coal and poor iron but much oil, silver, lead, zinc, copper, gold, graphite and antimony.

Canada can boast of great mineral wealth, including coal, nickel (almost a monopoly), gold, silver, copper, asbestos, lead, and zinc, great deposits of iron ore and oil. However, further prospecting will undoubtedly disclose new wealth. Twenty years ago a rich radium deposit was discovered on the Arctic Circle in Canada.

There are few countries rich in both coal and iron, the most fundamental of all minerals. Leading such a list of the fortunate are the United States, Great Britain, France, Russia-Siberia, and pre-war Germany. Based upon coal, oil, and gas our own country develops one half of the world's energy, "does one half the work of the world." Water power,

Am. Cyanamide Co.

FIG. 86. Mountains of ore yield to chemical processes.

incidentally, accounts for only four per cent of this country's industrial energy, and is actually exceeded by natural gas.

We can truthfully, if not modestly, declare that the United States leads in production of coal, iron, oil, gas, copper, lead, zinc, aluminum, sulfur, molybdenum, borax, cadmium, and sometimes leads in phosphates. We lack, however, some of the "key metals" which, in relatively small tonnage, are vital to large industries. We have imported the nickel, tungsten, vanadium, chromium, and manganese essential to alloy steels, but we can soon become the world's largest producer of chromium. Military wisdom dictates the accumulation of two years' supply for emergencies, a policy not unknown to France and other powers. Very wisely we are using more molybdenum in alloy steels, replacing tungsten in part. We have almost a monopoly on molybdenum ores.

This country lacks tin for tin cans, and produced only half of her potassium salts needed for permanent agriculture. However, Texas and New Mexico now give us the desired

The Midvale Company.

FIG. 87. The chemical industry is a great consumer of metals and alloys.

complete independence in the potash field. Limestone and clays are so common in most countries that they have not been discussed.

Maneuvering by the Powers for control of the world's mineral resources is not new and goes on with long-range vision into the future. This was the basis of certain political moves in North Africa by France, Germany, Italy, Spain and

Great Britain and was one of the bases for early Japanese action in the Orient. Germany's hazardous dash into Roumania during World War I was an effort to capture great oil fields. The Treaty of Versailles paid more attention to racial, historic, and political boundaries than to those suggested by wise mineral combinations.

There is also a steady drift towards control of minerals by a few powerful corporations, sometimes in full partnership with governments. Corporation control is, however, not an unmixed evil for it tends to conserve resources and to develop low grade ores. Consider the brilliant research that gave the world "flotation" of minerals. Think of working ores carrying only one per cent copper, as we do in this country. The ore, a sulfide of copper, is concentrated by roasting and other devices but first a wet slime is agitated with a trifling amount of pine oil and certain helpful chemicals so that a temporary froth is produced. Fortunately the copper sulfide particles stick to the oily films of the froth and are "floated" in defiance of gravity while the waste rock likes water better and so sinks to the bottom. This colloid chemical achievement has added many millions of dollars to the wealth of the world and will always be a conservation measure. With variations flotation is used in the concentration of other poor ores.

Another wise conservation device is the reclaiming of scrap or "secondary metals." For example old steel bridges, boilers and the like are cut up into convenient pieces by use of a blowtorch, shipped to the steel mill and worked into new steel. Old automobiles are robbed of their copper, aluminum, and other worth-while parts, to be converted into new metal again.

Substitutes are needed to save depleted stocks of metals. Aluminum is replacing 900,000 miles of copper cables in transmission of electric power; liquid fuels to be made from coal will replace oil in time; nitrates made from the air are already substituting for the dwindling reserves of Chile saltpeter (sodium nitrate); and powerful aluminum alloys are replacing steel in the transportation field. What shall we do without tin for food containers? Glass is breakable, gold plating of steel is effective but too expensive. Doubtless lacquer films will be made that will stand the heat of sterilization and aluminum coating of steel will serve in some instances.

The metallurgy of iron and steel may be taken as a good type for consideration here. Like many other ores iron occurs as oxide, carbonate, and sulfide. English ores are carbonates but in our own great ore beds of the Lake Superior district,

FIG. 88. Ancient Greek stack furnace.

Alabama, Colorado, the iron oxide called hematite is of leading importance. The problem is to steal the oxygen from the iron and this is accomplished in the gigantic steel tower, lined with fire brick, called a blast furnace or "stack." Some of these are 100 feet high and produce over 1,000 tons of crude iron (pig iron) daily. Hot carbon is selected as the oxygen thief although it is aided by carbon monoxide gas evolved in the burning of the coke.

The process might be termed "uproarious" for a regular tornado of hot air (50,000 cubic feet per minute) is blown in near the bottom of the stack to hurry up the burning of the coke, to raise the temperature to a point at which the crude pig iron liberated from its ore will melt and run out a tap hole at the bottom (periodically). Since there is a good deal of clay and other impurities in the ore limestone is charged in the top of the stack along with the coke and iron ore. The limestone reacts with clay and some other material to form an easily fusible slag which also falls to the bottom and is tapped off without mixing with the melted iron.

$$C + O_2 \rightarrow CO_2, \text{ carbon dioxide,}$$
$$CO_2 + C \rightarrow 2CO, \text{ carbon monoxide,}$$
$$Fe_2O_3 + 3CO \rightarrow 3CO_2 + 2Fe, \text{ iron,}$$
$$2Fe_2O_3 + 3C \rightarrow 3CO_2 + 4Fe.$$

This pig iron is brittle and hard and, although suitable for many objects of cast iron, needs to be converted into steel when great strength and some elasticity are desired.

The simplest method involves the removal (usually by oxidation) of impurities dissolved in the pig iron, followed by addition of from 0.1 of one per cent to 1.6 per cent of carbon. This is the simplest steel but practically all the steel made today has received valuable additional properties by enrichment with more or less manganese, chromium, nickel, or vanadium.

The primitive steel-making process of a thousand years or so ago was similar to "puddling," the heating of a ball of pig iron on a bed of iron ore. The oxygen of the ore united with the sulfur and other impurities objectionable in crude iron to form sulfur dioxide gas, etc., which escaped. This dough-like mass of purified iron was then hammered and squeezed until thin threads of "slag" in very small amount were well mixed with the iron but most of the slag squeezed out. The "wrought iron" formed was tough enough for anchors and horseshoes. Addition of a very little carbon would convert this iron into steel, or failure to oxidize all the carbon originally taken up by the iron from the coke in the blast furnace would leave a crude steel.

But steel making was slow and limited in size of batches until half a century or more ago when Kelley in the United States and Bessemer in England invented the "Bessemer convertor." In this huge steel, but fire-brick lined vessel, air was blown through 15 tons of melted pig iron burning out the sulfur, etc., with a dazzling shower of sparks lighting the midnight sky for many miles. In 15 minutes good steel was made, ready for railroad construction at reasonable prices. In fact without the invention of the Bessemer process just in time our vast railway conquest of the West would have been long-delayed for economic reasons. Later the Siemens open-hearth furnace produced better steel on a large scale by a process quite reminiscent of the puddling furnace. Preheated air and gas burning against a low ceiling directly over the pig

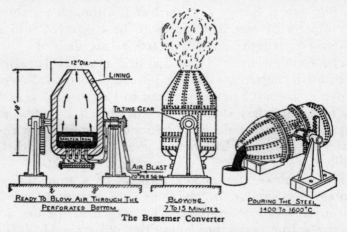

The Bessemer Converter

FIG. 89. The Bessemer converter making steel from pig iron. From a series of lantern slides by J. O. Frank and the Welch Scientific Co.

iron furnished the temperature while a bed of iron oxide (from ore and rusty scrap metal) furnished the oxygen for the burning out of impurities. Final addition of carbon and such elements as manganese completed the process as the steel was poured into molds.

At this time steel statistics are misleading but it may be of interest to note that in busy years the United States produces 120,000,000 tons of steel, nearly half of the total for the world.

The heat treatment and rolling of steels gives wide variation in useful properties. Sudden chilling of very hot steel produces great hardness while slow cooling of heated metal produces toughness. All this is a matter of the formation of

CARBON CONTENT OF STEELS

0.1 per cent......................	wire, chain, nails
0.08-0.18 per cent................	boilers
0.10-0.20 " "	screws, rivets
0.35-0.45 " "	axles, shafts
0.70-0.80 " "	cold chisels, jaws for vises
1.00-1.10 " "	tools for lathes, springs
1.20-1.30 " "	files
1.50-1.60 " "	saws for cutting steels

crystalline compounds of iron and carbon, or other things, or of uniform solutions. The chemist can polish a steel surface, etch it with a reagent that attacks only a part of the mixture called steel, and examine the etched surface with the microscope. Crystalline patterns revealed tell the whole story and make possible a scientific study of the structure of steels and alloys in general.

A single outstanding property of iron, magnetism, made possible the dynamo, motor, telegraph, telephone, compass— opened the gates for the entrance upon the scene of the whole electrical industry.

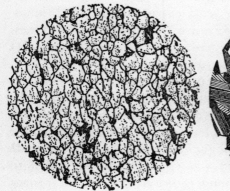 

FIG. 90.

The microstructure of polished and etched surface of alloy steel.   Microphotograph of the polished and etched surface of brass.

XXXIII

THE THREE LIGHT
METALS

THERE ARE only three possible light metals for engineering construction, aluminum, magnesium, and beryllium, and the third of these is still too expensive for practical use. Lithium is lighter but the violence of its reaction with water rules it out of the competition. For that matter lithium is soft and weak. In fairness we must admit the possibility of its use in alloys with other metals but such use seems unimportant. Sodium resembles lithium.

Aluminum makes up eight per cent of the earth's crust, is more plentiful than iron, but it holds on too tenaciously to the other elements associated with it in clay and bauxite for cheap extractions. Oerstedt, the Dane, first made it in 1825 followed by the German, Wöhler, in 1827, and there the matter rested for over sixty years except for the small industry founded by Deville in France. So costly was this new metal, $160 per pound for many years, that Napoleon III wore an aluminum helmet as a distinction of royalty.

The greatest scientists of Europe tried in vain to discover a cheap commercial process of preparing the metal. Metallic potassium, and later sodium, were used to steal the chlorine away from aluminum chloride but at what cost! Reduction of the oxide with carbon (analogous to reduction of iron oxide to iron in the blast furnace) was tried without success until in the '80's, when the high temperature of the electric furnace made this reaction possible. Unfortunately at these temperatures the desired aluminum was near its boiling point and had to be captured with copper so that only a copper alloy resulted. Electrolysis of water solutions of aluminum salts yielded only the oxide or hydroxide and electrolysis of melted cryolite did not quite succeed.

Finally a lad of twenty-two years, just graduated from Oberlin College, triumphed where scientific giants had failed. Inspired by a lecture comment of Professor Jewett's on the remarkable properties of aluminum and the importance of a cheapening of its cost, Charles Martin Hall nudged the boy next to him and whispered "I'm going for that metal." The going was not so good, however, and young Hall went often

FIG. 91. The youthful Charles M. Hall completes his great discovery of the modern aluminum process in his father's woodshed at Oberlin (1886).

to his sympathetic, helpful teacher for information, advice, and loans of batteries or other materials. After graduation the inventor worked on for several months in his father's woodshed at Oberlin and on February 23, 1886, achieved a brilliant success. Hurrying over to the old chemical laboratory (now gone like the historic woodshed) the eager young chemist held out his hand on which lay a few silvery lumps and said, with ill-suppressed excitement: "Professor, I've got it!"

By a remarkable coincidence another young man of twenty-two, Heroult in France, independently made the same discovery and applied for a French patent exactly two months after Hall's success.

Hall had melted cryolite, a double fluoride of aluminum

and sodium, in a graphite crucible, had dissolved in the liquid rock some aluminum oxide, and passed an electric current through the solution. After several failures his faith was justified—the shining metal separated, and the world was richer. So was Hall, ultimately, and the Aluminum Company of America, and Oberlin College to which Hall willed property worth, perhaps, $15,000,000.

The phenomenal growth of the industry is shown by the increase from a world production of 40,000 pounds in 1890 to 4,000,000 tons in 1955, probably to be doubled in 1975. Of this 1955 total the United States accounted for 1,500,000 tons while Canada, the nearest competitor, made nearly as much and other countries did extremely well. Canadian production, at low power cost, was originally owned by the parent organization, the Aluminum Company of America, which operates bauxite mines in Arkansas, and in British and Dutch Guiana in South America. The Canadian corporation has developed millions of horse power on the Saguenay River in Quebec and nearly as much at Kitimat out West. This power would be sufficient for the usual world demand for aluminum, yet this metal is finding so many new uses that great expansion may well be expected in the industry. Military aviation demands have forced a sudden vast increase in production.

The war demands for American aluminum production now exceed 2,000,000,000 pounds, placing this metal second to steel in tonnage, passing copper and zinc. Copper dates back over 5000 years; lead pipe may still be seen in ancient Roman palaces; and iron and zinc have a history of a few thousand years. Aluminum, however, is a mere infant in comparison with these ancient metals. Imagine the size of the aluminum industry in another century!

What are the properties of aluminum that have brought it into general use, even at 25 cents per pound? "Aluminum competes with gravity, corrosion, heat and electrical conductivity, as well as workability." There it is, very pithily expressed.

Pound for pound (but not volume per volume) it conducts electricity better than copper. Consequently there are in use today 900,000 miles of aluminum cable carrying electrical power.

One important modern development in applications is found in architectural uses. The shining cap, 100 ounces in weight, placed on the Washington Monument in 1884, pointed the way in two senses. Now the gleaming towers of Manhattan are adorned with many tons of aluminum spandrels connecting the windows in beautiful panels soaring upward. Window frames, copings, doorways, grille work, chairs of welded hollow framework, and even a lace-like Gothic church tower in Pittsburgh indicate that aluminum is to be reckoned

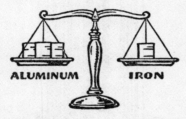

FIG. 92. Why aluminum is competing with steel.

with in modern architecture. One sixth of the exterior surface of the ten buildings in the Rockefeller "Radio City" was made of aluminum, 3,000,000 pounds of it. For small houses aluminum shingles, light and permanent, are offered. Bedsteads of this metal threaten to displace brass and iron.

For special ornamental uses, as in chandeliers, a new coating of strongly adhering dyes has just come on the market. These are not enameled but deposited on electrolytically oxidized metal and show an abrasion resistance ten times as great as five coats of baked enamel.

The ordinary metal you see is 99.2 per cent pure, silicon and iron accounting for the rest. However, for the grid structure of giant airships the lightness of aluminum and the strength of steel are required. The invention of such alloys as duralumin, containing 95 per cent aluminum, 4 per cent copper, 0.5 per cent manganese, and 0.5 per cent magnesium, solved the problem, made possible the Akron, "the most interesting aluminum cocoon ever spun by man." Such alloys when wrought and heat-treated attain a breaking strength of 75,000 pounds per square inch, approaching the strength of mild steel. The great alloy authority, Zay Jeffries, holds that particles of copper or other hardening elements serve as "keys" to prevent slippage between the different crystal planes of the aluminum.

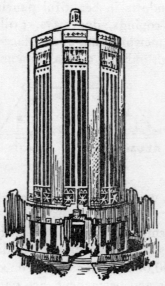

Fig. 93. Why not hide an ugly water tower within a decorative framework of aluminum.

To the great alarm of aircraft builders it was found that after continued exposure to the salt air above the ocean the duralumin frame of airships showed "intercrystalline corrosion," endangering the lives of passengers and crew. This difficulty, too, was overcome, by making the framework from an ingot of the powerful alloy coated with the twice-electrolyzed very pure aluminum, the whole mass rolled and shaped so that every surface presented to salt air the corrosion-resistant pure metal. There was no more intercrystalline corrosion.

A well-known use of the 99 per cent metal and its alloys is found in automobile construction. Many millions of aluminum pistons have been made as well as many other small parts. Aircraft needs the lightness of this metal and so do street cars and railway coaches and freight cars. One of the latest gondola cars saves ten tons in weight by the use of these light alloys for all parts except the trucks and couplers, and obviously can carry ten tons more freight. Several railroads are using aluminum in the construction of passenger coaches and the whole transportation industry is aluminum-conscious. Aluminum alloy trains driven 100 miles an hour by diesel-electric units are now in operation and more are ordered.

The swift-flying God, Mercury, must now be represented with aluminum wings on his feet. The air is filled with gleaming aluminum planes, lighter, larger, stronger, and more ambitious in their cruising range because of aluminum. One experimental plane was planned to carry 100 men or 14 tons of freight thousands of miles without refueling, thanks in part to weight saved by light aluminum and magnesium alloys. Remotest regions will become neighbors by flights of such planes. If desired, even larger and faster planes can be built. Aluminum birds have wrested the supremacy of the air from eagle and condor, falcon and gull.

A smooth, bright surface of aluminum is a splendid reflector of radiant heat and consequently the metal deserves its growing use as a heat insulator for locomotives, milk tanks, houses and naval vessels. Naturally the foil is just as efficient as heavy sheets and is lighter. A single ounce on the 200 inch telescope disk reflects invisible ultra-violet starlight on photograph film.

The earliest large use of this metal was in the manufacture of cooking utensils, still important and still quite safe to the user. There is only a trifling attack on the metal by the acids of cooking and the salts formed are harmless.

Flaked aluminum is a valuable pigment in paint, especially useful as a heat-reflecting covering for oil-storage tanks. Evaporation losses of gasoline in summer are greatly reduced

by such a silvery surface. It is to be hoped that public opinion
will force the use of aluminum paint on the hideous black gas
tanks that disfigure our cities. An aluminum surface blends
softly with blue sky.

Steel can now be coated with a thin film of aluminum,
thanks to the genius of Colin G. Fink, of Columbia University. After cleaning the surface of steel with hot hydrogen
the simple operation of dipping in molten aluminum produces

Science Service

FIG. 94. The terrific heat of the thermit reaction can loosen ice jams.

an adherent, protective coating. Although a section of a large
steel beam fairly burned in air at 1000° C. a similar section
coated with aluminum was as good as new after 1000 hours
of such treatment. Evidently structural steel so protected
would not break in hot fires. The aluminum apparently alloys
with the steel so that it does not melt at 1000° C. Here, also,
is a new type of rust-proof steel, with obvious uses.

Aluminum has come to the rescue more than once in
emergency welding of broken crank shafts or giant steel rolls
and broken steel parts in general. A mixture of granulated
aluminum with iron oxide is poured into a conical vessel just

above the broken parts and the reaction between the two chemicals started with a little ignition powder. Then the sparks fly. The plug in the cone is pulled and melted iron runs down on the broken parts.

$$2Al + Fe_2O_3 \rightarrow Al_2O_3 + 2Fe.$$

So great is the evolution of heat that the iron is more than melted as are the broken ends of the shaft. Of course a sand mould around the repair parts holds in the metal. A homogeneous weld results, strong as the original shaft.

Barnes of McGill University has used charges of thermit (the mixture of aluminum and iron oxide) to break dangerous ice jams in rivers. The terrific local heating weakens the jam at critical points. One jam of a million tons of ice at Ogdensburg, New York, was removed in nine hours with two ninety pound charges of thermit. He has even disintegrated an iceberg at sea by well placed thermit bombs.

Magnesium, driven by war demands in aviation, rose to an annual production of 150,000 tons. The price of 33 cents a pound will probably fall in ordinary competition. The metal is extracted from sea water, salt brines, dolomite, and magnesite. Since it is only two thirds as heavy as aluminum which sells at 25 cents a pound it looked like competition on a volume basis at least. Yet after all, these two metals work well together in certain types of alloys. Unlike aluminum, magnesium is hard.

Electrolysis of melted magnesium chloride to which has been added some salt to lower the melting point, produces metallic magnesium. Reduction of the oxide by carbon in the electric furnace may soon become a rival process, although this introduces the serious problem of chilling and condensing the inflammable magnesium vapor formed.

The so-called "milk of magnesia" used for medicinal purposes is a creamy suspension of magnesium hydroxide, $Mg(OH)_2$, in water. It is a very mild base. Basic magnesium carbonate, a fluffy white solid, saves the public enormous heat losses by covering steam pipes and boilers. A rival to asbestos, but all in the family, for asbestos rock is a magnesium calcium silicate. Fortunately for us there are great deposits of high-grade asbestos rock in Canada.

Beryllium is as light as magnesium, and its ores, such as beryl, are plentiful but unfortunately extraction of the metal is very costly. It is no stranger to the list of known metals for one could have bought it a century ago at a fortune for a pound and now it is reported that it may be bought at a few dollars a pound. Electrolysis of fused beryllium compounds is the method of manufacture but the process is beset with difficulties.

The metal is too brittle for use alone (except as the window in X-ray tubes) but in certain alloys it will certainly find service. The hardness and strength of copper are said to be increased several times by addition of a few per cent of beryllium. The electrical conductance is also increased somewhat. A copper-beryllium spring never shows fatigue, not even after 25,000,000 bendings, stands airplane vibration.

WEIGHT OF ONE CUBIC FOOT OF COMMON METALS

109 lbs.	169 lbs.	492 lbs.	556 lbs.	705 lbs.
Magnesium	Aluminum	Iron	Copper	Lead

In market price per cubic foot (not per pound) these metals in 1932 were very nearly the same, excepting iron which sold at a much lower price. Prices changed later.

NOTE. Only two per cent beryllium in nickel gives it the tensile strength of steel. Copper is hardened by it.

NOTE. Lithium, the lightest metal of all, was not given a place in this chapter for its uses were trifling. Yet in 1943 it was volatilized to yield a suitable non-oxidizing atmosphere for heat-treatment of steel. As a result there was no oxide scale to be cleaned off.

XXXIV

THE HOUSE OF THE FUTURE

THE PIONEERING days of this country are gone. The Western frontier has been pushed into the Pacific Ocean. We have killed most of the Indians and practically all of the buffalo and grizzly bears.

The westward march of empire provided a steady expansion of business, gave occasion for the great era of railroad building which in turn forced the tremendous growth of the steel industry. Then came the automobile, putting new blood into the veins of business, new roads on the map.

But now we have enough steel railways (perhaps too many), nearly as many concrete roads as the country can afford, 60,000,000 automobiles. The whole country could suffer if a mighty productive capacity, geared to continuing expansions, found markets glutted. Business cries for some vast new need that will keep factory wheels humming with pleasing music for years to come.

Better and cheaper houses for the average man, even for the poor man, will provide this vast market for the steel industry, the glass industry, the cement industry and a dozen others.

It may be objected that the country is already supplied with houses and apartments. The objector should read in *Fortune* of an earlier year, the pessimistic description of these houses. It was asserted that less than half the homes of America measured up to minimum standards of health and decency. The building industry, once complaining of overproduction, has just now started to build good homes within the means of two thirds of the population.

There has been, in recent years, a rapid increase in the average income of American families but building costs have also risen by a corresponding amount. "No family should buy a house costing more than twice its annual income and no family should pay more than twenty per cent of a limited income for rent."

Accepting this rule as a sound business guide, where will two thirds of our great population look for attractive, comfortable houses costing from $5,000 to $10,000? Excellent vision will be needed for those homes are at the end of the rainbow. Had the automobile industry limited its efforts to cars selling above $3,000 the industry would still be of moderate proportions only. Archaic building methods and the short-sighted tyranny of building trades unions have maintained high costs. A new industrial revolution is needed for the benefit of the common people. The stake is huge, a total volume of many billions for the building industry of 1956, greater than the railroad revenue, twice the value of the automobiles produced in that year.

To increase this several-fold will require the genius of the engineer, with an artistic touch, to solve problems and cut costs by factory methods. Able designers, great corporations, are at work on the problem—and they are optimistic.

Materials, some old and some new, are at hand. Structural steel, welding torches, light and strong aluminum alloys, steel sheets coated with delicately colored enamels, beautifully colored glass bricks, light aluminum or decorative copper roofing, cements, heat insulation of various types, tiles, asbestos, lacquers, glass that admits the healthful ultra-violet of sunlight, and adhesives that hold wood veneers to sheet steel are ready for builders. Plywood is the latest.

Europe has led the way in a field where America was expected to pioneer. Germany is using steel, glass, and concrete to build churches, stores, apartments, theaters, and homes with new and startling architectural lines. There was in Hungary a house with copper walls on the outside, steel on the inside, and heat insulation between these layers. It attracted much attention.

Forward-looking engineers tell us that these metal-and-glass houses of the near future must be built with complete disregard of long cherished building traditions. The first automobiles copied the archaic buggy to a considerable degree but at last a new art developed, suited to the needs of the present time. So should it be with houses. Today we demand plenty of light, air, comfort, cleanliness and living conveniences, and a new type of house may serve us best. As Walter Teagle put it:

"It is true that people lived full lives without any of this 'essential' equipment. The Tudor squires and Norman farmers who planned our houses for their own lives were stout fellows, often. They had to be: for fully half their

FIG. 95. The house of the future will break with tradition.

babies died, they suffered from bad teeth, rheumatism and gout, were contentedly unbathed, accepted smallpox and the Plague as inevitable, and had a life-expectation of thirty years as against our sixty-eight. . . . Our grandmothers lived very well without gas ranges, washing and ironing machines, electric toasters and refrigerators. But they also paid the help ten dollars a month and could take their pick. Today more homes than businesses are wrecked by labor troubles."

Probably some of the mass-production homes of low cost will be ugly, but so were the early automobiles. Beauty soon followed in the field of transportation. Beauty, simplicity, utility, and cleanliness are the modern standards for homes. These can be obtained at low cost only by factory methods. This does not condemn us to absolute uniformity of design, for welded units, whole rooms, may be arranged in different combinations just as a set of toy building blocks may be used to construct castles, bridges, houses.

Cellars will no longer be needed, nor expensive foundations, nor walls from eight to thirteen inches thick. Walls will be mere curtains, suspended by a steel or aluminum alloy framework. These walls of two skins of sheet metal, rustless steel, aluminum, copper, or enamel coated steel, with a sandwich filling of heat-insulating material, will be only an inch or two in thickness and yet they will keep out winter's cold and summer's heat more effectively than the heavy walls of the present.

Flat roofs, impossible in earlier days because of the weight of snow, will be common because structural metal will give all the strength needed. These flat roofs will become roof-gardens, where space is at a premium. Recessed stories may provide attractive terraces, also gardened to some extent.

With homes of higher cost, greater beauty and comfort will be possible. Translucent (not transparent) walls of tinted glass will admit plenty of soft light by day and glow like softly luminous flowers at night.

The greatest comfort and efficiency will come with "manufactured weathers," already produced for the President and Congress of these United States, hundreds of motion picture houses, certain factories with special needs, some trains, and some stores. Ventilation engineers have come to the conclusion that we feel most comfortable and are most efficient at about 70° F. and 35 to 40 per cent relative humidity, with a very gentle circulation of the air. Perhaps we should pause and explain what we mean by relative humidity. You know that dew falls when moist air is cooled considerably. This fact shows you that warm air can hold more moisture than can cold air. Conversely if cold winter air, saturated with moisture (100 per cent relative humidity), is brought into a house warmed to 70° F. the air will feel dry because warmer air can hold more moisture. Actually the relative humidity of the average home in very cold weather falls below 25 per cent of saturation, is dryer than air over the Sahara Desert. The mucous membranes of the nose, mouth, and throat suffer by too rapid evaporation of moisture and our chances of catching colds increase. It is no easy thing to add enough water to the air of our homes in winter. Six gallons a day are required by the average small house in freezing weather and twenty gallons or more in zero weather.

Air-conditioning plants wash the dust (and most bacteria) out of air with a spray of water which, at the same time,

Insulated Steel, Inc.

FIG. 96. Aluminum alloys and stainless steel give the world a new type of house.

humidifies the air. In summer it is proposed that this water spray be chilled by suitable refrigeration and the whole process handled so that a house with tight windows and excellent heat insulation will be delightful and stimulating while outside the neighbors swelter helplessly at 98° F. or worse. But to accomplish all this economically for the home of the future means that each house must be built like an ice-box. Much of the air will be recirculated, washed, in order to keep down costs. What zest there will be to summer life for the man who sleeps in an air-conditioned house, rides in an air-conditioned train to his work in an air-conditioned office or factory and goes to an air-conditioned theater in the evening!

Please note that none of this is visionary. The equipment is on the market and in fast-growing use. With falling costs and the use of properly insulated walls, adoption on a vast scale is certain. It is already possible to have the same equipment deliver heat in winter and cold in summer.

The deepest mine in the world is now air-conditioned, down to its lowest level of 8380 feet. In this gold mine on the Rand, South Africa, the temperature rose to 100°-120° F. and the relative humidity to 90-100 per cent, an intolerable condition. With gold at $35 an ounce it pays to pump 400,000 cubic feet of dry, cool air down to the workers.

We know how to oxidize offensive odors in the factory by blowing the air through activated charcoal. The time is ripe now for the use of the same device in the kitchen to remove the pervasive odors of boiled cabbage and onions. A very small fan circulating the kitchen air gently through a layer of very porous charcoal is all that is necessary. Carbon catalyzes or aids the attack of most of these odors by oxygen of the air.

The social effect of ownership of attractive homes by more millions of people will be great. Home life will be more attractive, an interest in beauty everywhere will be fostered, and communism will be discouraged. Chemistry does much to make it possible.

As this edition goes to press a novel heat insulation material is announced. While a certain synthetic resin is still in the liquid stage, air is beaten into it until it sets to a porous solid, suitable for wall insulation of houses in hot climates. It is more effective than cork or glass wool.

XXXV

HAVE YOU A CHEMIST
ON YOUR BOARD?

A FEW years ago one of the strongest of the oil companies boasted that four of the ten members of the Board of Directors were chemists, not engineers, but men trained in "pure," or theoretical, chemistry and rewarded with the Ph.D. degree. The President of the company was one of these Ph.D.'s, a man who won his spurs with a research development that, in a period of ten years, flooded the coffers of his company with approximately $100,000,000. Needless to add that this scientist was an able executive and shrewd business man.

This company was one of the first in the United States to build up a large staff of research chemists, following the lead of Germany where chemistry and industry had long been successful partners. The duPont Company and the General Electric were also among the great American organizations pioneering in research as the foundation of industry. They seem to be surviving.

World War I completed our conversion to the industrial and military importance of chemical research and now we lead the world in this respect. H. G. Wells was arresting rather than amusing when he declared, "The evolution of war is abolishing the soldier altogether and substituting the scientist."

Today we boast of thousands of research laboratories. Industry employs over 60,000 chemists and spends $3,000,-000,000 yearly on research and development.

Research is one of the safest forms of insurance for capital invested in industry. As Maurice Holland says, "In the highly competitive struggle for industrial supremacy, the march of science, discovery, and invention has so speeded up the advances of technology that a laboratory discovery may mean creation of a new industry, or expansion of one and losses for another." Research can create or destroy wealth. It is sound business practice, unfortunately not universal, to utilize the year of depression as research preparation for new and better and cheaper products. The industrial times are in a state of flux and nothing but eternal vigilance can continue to show a profit. "Quality is improved, production is increased, and costs are lowered by chemical research," says Esselen.

About half of a century ago great banks in Germany consulted able chemists before making loans to manufacturers, believing as they did that a close coöperation between research and production was necessary to the safety of the loan. Somewhat hesitatingly American bankers have come to see the wisdom of such a far-sighted policy.

The world production of chemicals is said to be worth many billions and these chemicals are essential to the success of other industries. In our own country petroleum products total 2,700,000,000 barrels, not ordinarily termed "chemical products." We insist that petroleum refining is a chemical process and that the manufacture of iron and steel products amounting to over 120,000,000 tons in the United States is also a chemical process. We might also claim the enormous synthetic fiber industry, the million tons of synthetic rubber, the 1,500,000 tons of plastics and products of other giant industries. The products of all our chemical process industries are valued at $60,000,000,000 yearly.

For every dollar spent in agricultural research the nation profits to the extent of $500; and $25,000,000 is appropriated annually by the Federal Government and the states for this work. Some years ago the Capper prize of $5000 was presented to Professor Stephen M. Babcock of the University of Wisconsin for the most distinguished service to American agriculture. In 1890, this man gave the world the famous Babcock test for butter fat in milk and made the dairy industry honest, stable, and scientific. As a result herds were graded up in quality and literally hundreds of millions of dollars added to the wealth of the nation. No great organization financed Babcock so the percentage of profit is beyond computation.

"Patient money" is the wisest money when it comes to research. Results can not be guaranteed overnight, as some of our driving manufacturers have finally realized. A great

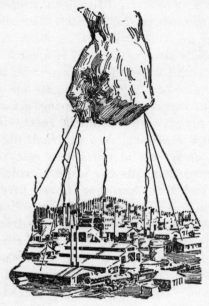

FIG. 97. "Business holds industry in its hand but without research control that hand trembles."

German dye company poured $5,000,000 over a space of twenty years into the search for a commercial method of synthesizing indigo. Their patience and wisdom were rewarded with an industry producing $20,000,000 worth of artificial indigo annually.

And it pays to subsidize theoretical research as well as efforts that promise to lead directly to dividends. Pupin's loading coil for the telephone circuit, invented forty years ago, is said to have produced a total saving of $500,000,000 in copper wire. Faraday's "pure" research a century ago had much to do with the founding of the gigantic electrical industry. The General Electric Company wisely let Langmuir ramble through the fields of research wherever his fancy led him. They knew their man, of course. His theoretical work, however, turned out to have enormous practical value, saving the people of this country many millions of dollars every year.

Millikan declares that one Michelson, eminent as a "pure" physicist, is worth more to this country than any billion dollar corporation. But we seem to be getting away from chemistry.

"Research made your motor car" is a catch phrase, yet an accurate one. Extend it to the airplane, the airship, and it still holds true. Rubber, alloy steel, gasoline engine, aluminum, magnesium, lacquer, non-shattering glass, storage battery—all were prepared by chemical reactions or functions by the aid of such reactions. And the fuel, the lubricant, are direct products of successful petroleum research. In accordance with changing demands the same petroleum now yields much gasoline and little kerosene where fifty years ago it was valued mainly for kerosene with gasoline as an undesirable by-product. In this as in other industries the research staff anticipates changes and prepares for them.

The next time you enjoy a "talkie" remember that successful research here forced the expenditure of $500,000,000 for new equipment. The old movie lot offered no chair to a weary research man; now they fairly clutter up the place. Research is good business. Again we must admit that these later developments are not chemical, yet the film itself is absolutely a chemical product. As you learned in the chapter on cellulose, the nitration of that material gave the world the movie film of celluloid, an artificial silk, automobile lacquer and, when varied in degree, guncotton and smokeless powder. Finally business demanded cheaper acetic acid (and its anhydride) so that the non-inflammable celluloid made from cellulose acetate could be given universal use. It's up to the chemist, of course.

Many years ago the Japanese decided to levy a heavy

toll on the movie industry by pushing up the price of natural camphor of which they had a monopoly. Camphor was considered necessary to celluloid. Research developed an artificial camphor from turpentine and the price of the Formosan product fell at once. Now we are making our own camphor.

Southern Pacific

FIG. 98. Coronado's soldiers of Spain searched our western coast for "cities of turquoise, pearl, and gold" more than two centuries before gold was actually discovered in California.

Do you realize that a leader in the rubber industry, Dr. William Geer, said that the discovery of accelerators in the vulcanizing of rubber saves this country fully $400,000,000 yearly—primarily in the time of vulcanization, eventually in cost? If the railroads succeed in recapturing traffic by putting automobiles with flanged rubber wheels on railroad tracks they should unite in employing a great sculptor to erect a statue to Goodyear, whose research made rubber useful.

Some of these facts we have told you in earlier chapters but repetition of outstanding points is the essence of good teaching. May we urge you to read again, if you will, of the business importance of alloy steels in the building industry and the automobile industry; of aluminum, magnesium, copper; of cellulose products; of formaldehyde and carbolic acid (phenol) in the manufacture of bakelite; of the synthesis of ammonia from the air and its conversion into nitric acid for explosives, or fertilizing salts for agriculture; of American independence in the dye industry, so important to our vast textile industry; and of the chemical products from coal?

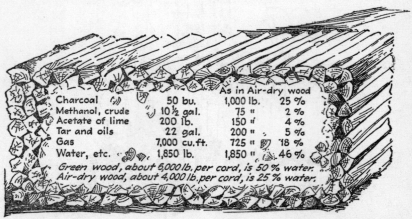

		As in Air-dry wood	
Charcoal	50 bu.	1,000 lb.	25 %
Methanol, crude	10½ gal.	75 "	2 %
Acetate of lime	200 lb.	150 "	4 %
Tar and oils	22 gal.	200 "	5 %
Gas	7,000 cu.ft.	725 "	18 %
Water, etc.	1,850 lb.	1,850 "	46 %

Green wood, about 5,000 lb. per cord, is 50 % water.
Air-dry wood, about 4,000 lb. per cord, is 25 % water.

FIG. 99. Retort distillation of wood, directly or indirectly, yields methyl alcohol, acetone, acetic acid and a grade of charcoal indispensable in making certain superior steels.

You have heard, of course, that about 1925 our $100,-000,000 hardwood distillation industry was threatened with ruin because some research chemists in Europe learned how to make pure wood alcohol (CH_3OH) from water gas. Now we have brought that synthesis to America and are making great quantities of this useful product at a very low cost. Even the acetone and acetic acid, formerly made by wood distillation, are now prepared by other chemical methods. Apparently no industry dares to stand still.

We are watching with interest the thousands of miles of new welded pipe lines for carrying high-pressure natural gas to distant cities. Will not this mean the ultimate coking of coal at the mine, the conversion of coke and nearly all the other products into fuel gas, followed by pressure piping to cities a thousand miles away? The railroads will object—but cities will become smokeless and more beautiful.

Be careful not to speak of "useless" elements and museum specimens. They said that of tungsten up to about fifty

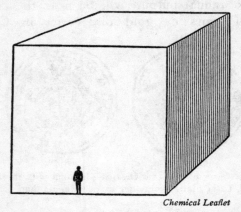

Chemical Leaflet

FIG. 100. All the gold mined since the discovery of America would make, at best, a cube 38 ft. on edge.

years ago but now it is called a "key metal," vital to industry. Tungsten lamps give us so much more light with so much less electricity used that the national saving in electric light bills is fully $500,000,000 every year. All because some research worker learned how to make ductile tungsten filaments that would not break with ordinary use. And you pay much less for your car because machine tools of tungsten steel can be worked on the lathe until they are red hot, with no loss of temper or cutting edge. The High Speed Age is the Tungsten Steel Age. Tellurium is practically useless today but do you dare predict that it will be useless tomorrow? Research will settle that question.

And now what about the yardstick of business success, Gold?

Since the discovery of America, 45,000 tons of gold have

been produced in the world, enough to make a solid cube 38.5 feet high. Most of this precious metal has gone out of circulation into the arts and crafts or into hoarded reserves of India and other countries. In times when more gold is badly needed in order to regulate the price level of commodities we are faced with the gloomy prediction that in fifteen years the gold mines of South Africa, which now supply the world with over half the annual output, will be near the end of their production. Rumors of gold discoveries in Canada and

The Tiffany Co.

FIG. 101. A counterfeiter once plated cheaper platinum with the more expensive gold. Later platinum became more valuable than gold.

Sweden are encouraging and no doubt the lowered costs of gold production could make it profitable to reopen many mines closed during the era of inflated costs. Unfortunately this corrective influence of the ebb and flow of gold mining upon prices of commodities in general is uncomfortably slow in action. The discovery of the cheap cyanide process of gold extraction many years ago made it possible to work ores too poor for the previous methods and thus added enormously to world stocks of the metal. The record is held by an Alaskan mine that continues to extract gold from an ore carrying less than one dollar's worth of the metal to the ton. Business will be interested if another chemical improvement should be discovered.

"As a basis of exchange, greatly facilitating the development of commerce among the peoples of the earth, the value of gold to civilization exceeds all reckoning."

It is interesting to learn that the price of silver depends

upon its use as money, that if India attempts to go upon the gold standard, silver prices slump. Engineers contend that it should be sold as a commodity, bringing a few cents more per pound than copper because it is a better conductor of electricity and would, within production limits, replace copper in the electrical industry. Photography and the arts use only a small part of the world production. At the present silver is chiefly a by-product of the copper and lead industries.

Platinum was once used for coins in Russia and it is not impossible that this precious metal may some day displace gold as the standard of values. There is not enough at present to do the world's work in science, industry and the arts but modern prospecting in South Africa indicates the existence of a vast platinum "reef."

Tradition should not always dictate the course of wisdom. Perhaps business, like science, will look at the future with an open mind.

"Seeing tomorrow in the test tube" is a good slogan. In 1941 we consumed 10 billion dollars' worth of products unknown before 1918, so it behooves us to be on the alert for similar rapid changes in the near future.

In a few years most passenger cars will use 90-100 octane gasoline instead of the old 72 octane, and get 25 miles per gallon. The banker, the investor must know a little chemistry. He must remember that chemists in giving us synthetic camphor not only gave us independence of Japan in this key substance of the photographic industry but cut the price from exorbitant to reasonable. The same independence of silk and large price cut resulted with the perfection of nylon. In eight years our annual production of methyl alcohol for plastics, etc., changed from 500,000 gallons at $1.00 a pound to 25,000,000 gallons at 33 cents.

As a shrewd manufacturer put it, "Our frontiers of today are frontiers of science" (Tom Girdler).

XXXVI

STRATEGIC RAW MATERIALS

IN RECENT years the United States Government has published, with occasional revisions, lists of "strategic raw materials" (essential to the national defense), the supply of which comes in whole or in part from outside the boundaries of continental United States. For a time there were seventy items on this list, but invention of practical methods of utilizing certain low-grade domestic supplies, discovery of substitutes and large accumulation of stock piles held in reserve for emergencies, may shorten the list. War adds to it.

Aluminum	Optical glass
Antimony	Quartz crystal
Chromium	Quinine
Cobalt	Rubber
Manganese (ferro grade)	Silk
Mica	Tin
Mercury	Tungsten
Nickel	Wool

If worst came to worst in a blockade by enemies, we could still produce some of these items effectively or develop substitutes. The situation would be critical but not hopeless. However, all but the blind can see that stock piles of two years' supply would have a defensive power equal to that of several battleships—and would cost much less.

Of aluminum, we are the world's greatest producer. The importation from northern South America (the Guianas) of a considerable fraction of the bauxite ore required looks worse than it is. Arkansas bauxite, although not quite so pure, could carry us through any crisis. We have great deposits in Haiti and Jamaica as well as alunite in Utah, as reserve sources, less economically profitable, but reassuring. Aluminum is essential to aircraft, yet steel, copper and one or two other metals compete with it for many of its present uses—and could be substituted to a considerable degree.

Antimony, used in relatively small tonnage, is important in type metal (recovered by remelting) and in a few other alloys. Calcium can take its place as a stiffener for the lead grid in storage batteries. Most of our antimony, as the sulfide ore, comes from Asia, yet Mexico and the United States are producers.

Chromium and manganese, used in making nearly all our modern steels, gave us great concern. Normally we import 400,000 tons of chromite ore and produce little, due to the poor quality of native deposits. The Philippines have a great chromite ore bed but the Pacific Ocean separates us from that source. Cuba is near and its chromite may become a great help in emergencies, but the supply there will not meet our total needs. Rhodesia, India, Turkey, Russia, New Caledonia and Portuguese Africa, the most important sources, are far away. By 1943 the development of processes for concentrating low grade chromium ores in Montana promised to make this country less dependent.

The manganese situation is not so critical as the chromium problem, for we already produce quantities of low-grade ores as well as 1,200,000 tons of iron ores carrying from 5 to 10 per cent manganese, very useful in steel-making. Most of our needs are supplied by the richer ores from Brazil and Cuba. Russia and India are the world's greatest producers. With our domestic demand for manganese ores exceeding 1,000,000 tons annually, and with Cuba, Brazil and the United States together producing little more than half that amount, there is occasion for some concern about our steel industry, for one ton of steel requires 13 pounds of manganese.

Cobalt forms acid-resisting alloys with some metals, one important in exhaust valves of airplanes. We depend on Canada and South Africa for our supply.

Our native mica supplies are insufficient for our needs in electrical insulation, forcing us to import heavily from British India. A recent invention gives us an excellent synthetic mica for electronic devices, the "eyes, ears, and nerves of modern war."

Mercury for scientific uses, for detonating caps in high explosive shells, for dentistry, etc., is needed to the extent of about 1500 tons in this country, but we normally produce only one half of it. War needs seemed to force us to risk exhaustion of our ore beds.

Nickel, highly important to the steel industry and to electroplating to the extent of 60,000 tons annually, can all be supplied from Canada, not likely to be separated from us by an enemy. However, Canada must also supply Great Britain.

Optical glass of a few special types is imported, but our industry can expand to take care of nearly all our needs. The military uses of such glass in cameras, field glasses, periscopes, etc., are apparent.

Quinine gives us serious concern. Many thousand people die, many more are weakened every year in this country by malaria, and there are no perfect substitute medicines. Research offers one or two and they are said to be moderately good.

Natural rubber, to the extent of 600,000 tons yearly, was imported from the East Indies to supply us with tires for autos and airplanes and for a hundred other uses. Several synthetic rubbers based on petroleum or acetylene (from coal, limestone and water) are already in great production competing in cost with the natural product, but it took at least two years and great government financial support to expand such small industries adequately. Reclaimed rubber could help us to the extent of 200,000 tons of poorer material. See page 96 for a discussion of synthetic rubber.

Silk is being replaced by nylon for personal wear and for parachutes. Rayon bags now hold the gunpowder behind the great projectiles shot from cannon. Once we paid Japan more than $200,000,000 yearly for silk, but in the future this expenditure will never be more than a very small fraction of the former total.

Tin, like rubber, comes largely from the East Indies by an uncertain route, although Bolivia has arranged to supply us with some ore from her limited supply. We use 75,000 tons of this metal yearly and produce only 110 tons from Alaska. Tin-plating of our nineteen billion "tin cans" yearly takes 40 per cent of the total importation, solder and machinery bearings 30 per cent. Steel coated with aluminum by Fink's process, lacquered cardboard containers, glass jars, etc., could displace a substantial fraction of the tin-can use.

Tungsten, largely imported from China, is vital to the high-speed steel-cutting tools which permit faster work with lathes in so many vital industries. We produce some ores in Colorado and Arizona; will produce more. Molybdenum, of which we have plenty in Colorado, can be substituted for half the tungsten in such cutting tools.

Wool is largely but inadequately grown in the United States, forcing importation from Australia and Argentina. Some other countries, producing little wool, are making warm clothing from a treated casein fiber, with more or less success. Chemical research may, in time, give wool a real competitor.

There is another official list of "critical materials," less serious because we already produce several items or because they are less essential to the national defense.

Critical Materials

Asbestos	Iodine
Cadmium	Jute
Castor oil	Kapok
Coffee	Opium
Cork	Phenol
Cryolite	Platinum
Flaxseed	Scientific glass
Fluorspar	Tannin
Graphite	Titanium
Hides	Vanadium
Industrial diamonds	

We can depend on Canada for our platinum and asbestos. Recently we began to produce most of our own vanadium. With proper encouragement the castor bean could be grown in this country.

Among other "essential materials" which we produce in great quantities are abrasives, acetone, alcohol, arsenic, synthetic camphor, cotton (cellulose), chlorine, coal, copper, helium, iron and steel, petroleum, magnesium, lead, phosphates, potash, molybdenum, sulfur, wood and zinc. We are fortunate in possession of such vast resources.

A strange shortage developed in clear quartz crystals which in extremely thin sheets are a military necessity in radio communication. Brazil and new deposits in this country came to the rescue.

The end of our high-grade iron ore of the Lake Superior region is in sight, so it is good news that the extensive low-grade taconite Superior ores are now being beneficiated for effective use and that vast ore deposits in Quebec have been opened up.

Tropical kapok fiber for life jackets ran low. To meet the need Boris Berkman developed the floss of wild milkweed pods as an excellent substitute with a good prospect of finding peacetime use in light, warm clothing and blankets.

The government stockpile of strategic materials is now valued at $5,000,000,000 and will reach $7,000,000,000.

XXXVII

ATOMIC POWER. BOMBS

IF YOU WILL READ again pages 108 to 127 you will be well prepared for this chapter. However we will remind you that the atom is mostly space, like our solar system, with nearly all the weight or mass concentrated in the nucleus, which accounts for only a minute fraction of the atomic volume. Electrons revolve around the nucleus.

The nucleus is a powerfully bound little packet of positively charged protons and neutrons (which have no charge). Since there is only one proton in the nucleus of the hydrogen atom (lightest of all) and a steadily increasing number in all the atoms, up to 92 in heavy uranium, it is convenient to list elements by "atomic numbers" from 1 for hydrogen to 101 for the latest element created.

Atomic weights are also listed but they often involve annoying fractions. As you learned on page 120 most elements occur as mixtures of forms (isotopes), chemically alike but of somewhat different weights. Even hydrogen, although almost completely H-1, contains a little H-2 and the merest trace of H-3.

Now what is the meaning of $_{92}U$-238, so vital in the development of atomic power and of the related bombs? Simply that uranium is the 92nd heaviest element (atomic number 92) and that you are referring to the isotopic form weighing 238. This makes up nearly all of common uranium but the key to the whole exciting story of atomic fission is the accompanying $_{92}U$-235, which accounts for less than one per cent of common uranium.

But nothing exciting would have happened if the neutron had not been discovered—and tamed!

We owe discovery of the neutron to Chadwick in England

who, in 1931, bombarded beryllium with alpha particles, spontaneously emitted by polonium. The neutron's remarkable ability to penetrate matter is due to its lack of electrical charge. Such flying "bullets" are not repelled or deflected by positively charged nuclei and so may hit squarely.

The stage was set but the curtain was delayed until 1938 when Hahn and Strassmann in Germany seemed to have split the uranium atom into two or more fragments with a definite loss of mass and consequent release of energy. This was in line with Einstein's earlier prediction that matter could be converted into enormous amounts of energy.

It took a smart woman, Leise Meitner, to interpret the Hahn-Strassmann report. Others quickly confirmed this work. Undoubtedly Hahn built upon the fundamental research of Fermi, then in Italy.

Under the stress of war our own government placed vast sums at the disposal of famous chemists and physicists to investigate the military (explosive) possibilities. Development of bomb and power went on, hand in hand, with emphasis on the bomb.

To make the first atomic bomb required two and a half years of intensive work by 100,000 scientists and engineers—at a cost of $2,000,000,000.

It was soon found that uranium-235, less than one per cent of common uranium, was the "fissionable" part, broken into fragments with conversion of some mass into energy (as heat)—when its nucleus was hit by flying neutrons of the right velocity.

Fermi, working secretly under the athletic field of the University of Chicago, showed that fast neutrons had to be slowed down (by graphite or "heavy" water) to a speed permitting capture by the nucleus of the uranium-235 atom.

The first high hopes of the scientists at Chicago were dashed when they found that the reaction of any one atom of U-235 was promptly stopped by the preponderating atoms of apparently worthless U-238 which got in the way of a spreading of the fire.

Hopes had been pinned on the remarkable reaction:

U-235 + slow neutrons → Ba + Kr + 2 neutrons + heat

These extra neutrons resulting strike other U-235 atoms and so on in a chain reaction that could become instantaneous, and explosive, but for the blocking action of U-238. Meanwhile the unsuspecting college boys romped happily around Chicago's athletic field just over Fermi's head.

Tremendous efforts were made to separate the active U-235 and they were successful—at great cost.

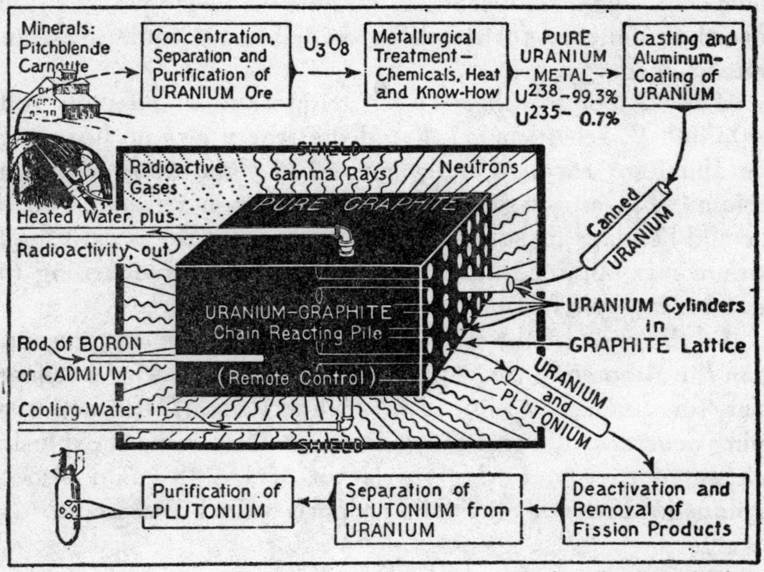

American Petroleum Institute

FIG. 102. Atomic power plant.

Early fears of a runaway reaction and explosion were allayed by discovery that rods of cadmium, pushed in and out of the lattice of uranium bars could control the dangerous reaction perfectly.

The atomic bomb was not practical until it was found that no explosion occurred unless a "critical mass" of U-235 was present. Naturally the first bomb contained a device for quickly bringing together smaller weights.

The next great discovery was that the supposedly worthless U-238 reacted with neutrons of the right velocity, in three steps, to yield a new element, number 94, plutonium-239, which in turn could be fissioned by neutrons of proper velocity and so could be utilized in an atomic bomb. The tough chemical problem of separating the plutonium-239 from the other material was solved.

THE HYDROGEN BOMB

Back in 1928 Aston in England had predicted that at sufficiently high temperatures atoms of hydrogen could be forced to unite to form helium, with loss of some mass and release of energy.

The "A-bomb" offered such temperatures, possibly 100,-000,000° F. Scientists calculated that there was no hope with the abundant form of hydrogen, H-1, some hope with deuterium, H-2, and a great deal of hope with tritium, H-3, if it could be made by some process unknown at the time. Finally tritium was obtained at an incredible cost by bombarding the unstable isotopic form of lithium, Li-6, with neutrons.

So the core of the hydrogen bomb, vastly more powerful than the A-bomb, must be the A-bomb as a source of adequate heat, surrounded by Li-6, which yields tritium. Then action of flying neutrons converts the tritium into helium with explosive release of energy. Perhaps a jacket of U-238 could also be exploded. However all this is properly veiled in secrecy.

THE MENACE

Aside from devastating heat flash, atomic radiations, and wave blast, there is the danger from clouds of radioactive dust blown far by winds. This dust could contaminate clothing, food, water supplies, buildings, etc., at great distances.

THE DEFENSE

Dispersal of important industries, radar warning systems, planned rapid evacuation of cities, bomb shelters have been proposed. However, fear of instant and effective retaliation may be our best defense. Now that we have atomic bombs small enough to be carried by planes and shot from field guns it is clear that Russia's great numerical superiority in troops has been discounted.

ATOMIC POWER

The first "reactor," potentially an atomic power plant if the heat generated had been utilized, was operated for the benefit of the hoped-for bomb.

The picture is changing rapidly with government and industry cooperating to build atomic power plants. Other countries, not so rich in coal as ours, may lead the way, notably Great Britain.

The possibility of cheap and limitless atomic power is thrilling, giving hope that many poor countries may become partly industrialized and thus raise their standard of living. To that end the United States is offering to share technical skill with smaller and less-favored countries.

How amazing that fission of one atom of uranium-235 releases fifty million times as much energy as the ordinary burning of one atom of carbon!

But commercial success in competing with coal as a fuel is not just around the corner. Plants now building are really just learning devices. With experience costs will be cut and perhaps in ten years large power plants at considerable distances from coal fields will be competitive. So rapidly does our demand for power of all sorts increase that for many years atomic power will merely supplement coal. In the end coal may be utilized mainly as a source of chemicals and liquid or gaseous fuel.

We now have two submarines powered with atomic reactors and probably will soon place reactors in the larger ships. Not, however, in autos and trucks because of high cost and the great weight of material to shield from dangerous radiations.

Perhaps we should have stated earlier that the heat generated in a reactor is used to convert water into steam to be used as in any conventional power plant.

Fuels. Uranium is not the only fuel for these plants for thorium also is fissionable.

It is suggested that a soluble salt of uranium could be dissolved in water which would turn into steam as reaction started. If costly "heavy water" is used the deuterium content would act as moderator.

Another suggestion is that a fused alloy of uranium and bismuth be made the fuel.

Coolants. Water (under pressure) or a fused alloy of sodium and potassium in a system of pipes could be used to carry away the heat to another system containing water for steam generation.

Construction Materials. Great sums are being spent to develop materials that will be better than steel for operating at high temperatures under intense atomic radiation. Zirconium, very difficult to separate from its ores, is desirable for it is strong, resists corrosion, has a high melting point and does not absorb neutrons.

Radioactive Wastes. The wastes from an atomic power plant present a serious problem. They are too dangerous to dump into streams, perhaps dangerous in the oceans, and certainly must not be thrown away in the deserts. Perhaps if fused with some sort of clay the stuff could be buried deep.

The best hope is to utilize radiations from these wastes in research and industry as is now done with certain radioactive isotopic forms of some elements.

Radioactive Isotopes. On exposure to a reactor many elements yield new isotopic forms that resemble radium in their radiations. In fact cobalt-60 is very effective in replacing costly radium once used to treat accessible cancer.

Other active isotopes (as soluble salts) are invaluble research tools in following the course of certain substances in plant and animal bodies. Medicine and agriculture benefit.

The Geiger counter, with its audible clicks, keeps track of these "tracer elements."

Many chemical reactions are influenced by radiations from such isotopes and industry is starting research in this field. Furthermore, their use in process control saved our industries $100,000,000 in 1955.

Truly atomic fission may, in the end, do more good than harm.

XXXVIII

WINNERS OF THE NOBEL PRIZE IN CHEMISTRY

THE Swedish Academy of Science annually awards a Nobel Prize of approximately $40,000 to the chemist who is judged to have contributed most to the benefit of mankind. It is interesting to note that Alfred Nobel, who gave several million dollars to the Nobel Foundation in 1896, was the man who invented dynamite.

Year	Winner	Country	Contribution
1901	J. H. van't Hoff	Holland	Theory of solutions, molecular structure.
1902	Emil Fischer	Germany	Proteins. Chemistry of sugars.
1903	Svante Arrhenius	Sweden	Theory of ionization.
1904	William Ramsay	England	Isolation of the rare gases of the air.
1905	Adolf von Baeyer	Germany	Synthesis of indigo.
1906	Henri Moissan	France	Isolation of fluorine. Electric furnace.
1907	Edouard Buchner	Germany	The chemistry of enzymes and fermentation.
1908	Ernest Rutherford (born in N. Zealand)	England	Radioactivity.
1909	Wilhelm Ostwald	Germany	Theory of solutions, fixation of nitrogen.
1910	Otto Wallach	Germany	Chemistry of the terpenes.
1911	Madame Curie (born in Poland)	France	Isolation of radium and polonium.
1912	V. Grignard	France	Special synthesis of organic compounds.
1912	P. Sabatier	France	Catalytic hydrogenation of fats, etc.
1913	Alfred Werner	Switzerland	Valence and chemical constitution.
1914	Theodore W. Richards	United States	Atomic weight determinations.
1915	R. Willstätter	Germany	Structure of chlorophyll.
1918	Fritz Haber	Germany	Synthesis of ammonia from its elements.
1920	Walther Nernst	Germany	Electrochemistry, thermodynamics.
1921	Frederick Soddy	England	Radioactive elements.
1922	Francis W. Aston	England	Discovery of isotopes.
1923	Fritz Pregl	Austria	Microanalysis of organic compounds.

Year	Winner	Country	Contribution
1925	Richard Zsigmondy	Germany	The chemistry of colloids, ultramicroscope.
1926	The Svedberg	Sweden	The chemistry of colloids.
1927	Heinrich Wieland	Germany	The chemistry of the bile acids.
1928	Adolf Windaus	Germany	Cholesterol and vitamins.
1929 {	Arthur Harden	England	Alcoholic fermentation, sugar, vitamins.
	von Euler-Chelpin	Sweden	Enzymes and vitamins.
1930	Hans Fischer	Germany	Production of hemin from hemoglobin.
1931 {	Carl Bosch	Germany	Fixation of nitrogen.
	Friedrich Bergius	Germany	Liquid fuels from coal; sugar from wood.
1932	Irving Langmuir	United States	Surface chemistry; atomic structure.
1934	Harold C. Urey	United States	Discovery of hydrogen of atomic weight two, and of "heavy water."
1935 {	Irene Curie-Joliot	France	Artificial radioactivity.
	F. Joliot		
1936	Peter Debye	Germany	Theory of complete ionization.
1937 {	Paul Karrer	Switzerland	Carotenoids. Vitamins.
	Walter N. Haworth	England	Carbohydrates. Vitamin C.
1938	Richard Kuhn	Germany	Carotenoids and vitamins.
1939 {	Adolph Butenandt	Germany	Sex hormones.
	Leopold Ruzicka	Switzerland	Sex hormones.
1943	Georg Hevesey	Hungary	Use of isotopes as indicators in studying chemical reactions.
1944	Otto Hahn	Germany	Discovery of a method of breaking the heavy atom nucleus.
1945	Artturi Wirtanen	Finland	Discoveries relating to agricultural and food chemistry.
1946 {	James B. Sumner	United States	Discovery that enzymes can be crystallized; crystallization of catalase and urease.
	John Northrop	United States	Crystallization of hydrolytic enzymes, pepsin, and related ones.
	Wendell M. Stanley	United States	Studies in virus research, showing that viruses are crystallizable proteins.
1947	Sir Robert Robertson	England	Research on life products of plants and animals, particularly the alkaloids.
1948	Arne Tiselius	Sweden	Discoveries in biochemistry and development of the electrophoretic method for studying proteins and other colloidal substances.
1949	William F. Giauque	United States	Research in the fundamental properties of matter at low temperatures.
1950 {	Otto Diels	Germany	Development of diene synthesis.
	Kurt Adler		

1951	{ Glenn T. Seaborg { Edwin M. McMillan	United States	Discovery of transuranium elements.
1952	{ Archer J. P. Martin { R. Millington Synge	England Scotland	Development of partition chromatography.
1953	Herman Staudinger	Germany	Development of chemistry of high polymers.
1954	Linus Pauling	United States	Work on the nature of chemical bonds.
1955	Vincent du Vigneaud	United States	Work on biochemically important sulphur compounds, especially for the first synthesis of a polypeptide hormone.
1956	{ Cyril Hinshelwood { Nikolai N. Semenov	England U.S.S.R.	Researches into the mechanism of chemical reactions.

The awards in chemistry were not made in 1916, 1917, 1919, 1924, 1933, 1940, and 1941.

INDEX

INDEX